CMOS
VLSI Layout Artwork
Design and Lab

Yong-Bin Kim Ph.D.

Department of Electrical and Computer Engineering
Northeastern University

MyCAD Press,
a division of MyCAD, Inc.
Sunnyvale, California 940

CMOS VLSI Layout Artwork Design and Lab
Yong-Bin KIM Ph.D.

Publisher : MyCAD Press
Editor-in-Chief : KG YANG
Associate editor : Mi-Ra LEE
Supplements editor : Ryan KWON
Designer : Sun-Hee PARK
Cover designer : Genie KIM
Manufacturing Manager : Dong-Ro CHOI

© 2002 by MyCAD Press
a division of MyCAD, Inc.
528 E. Weddell Drive, Suite 3
Sunnyvale, California 94089

Printed in the Republic of Korea

Library of Congress Cataloging-in-Publication data is pending.

ISBN 0-9727735-0-9

P *reface*

As the title suggests, this book is for CMOS VLSI Layout Design. Layout is the process of assigning geometric shapes, sizes, and positions to the components (transistors and connections) used in its fabrication. Since the number of components in modern VLSI is enormous, Computer-Aided-Design (CAD) programs are required to automate the difficult layout process.

CAD companies specialize in providing powerful CAD software for the entire VLSI design process. These workstation-based software tools cost a lot of money, but provide convenient and powerful features, even though it is not an easy task to maintain the software tools and database. On the other hand, CAD tools also exist for the PC. MyCAD's MyChip Station provides a complete IC layout CAD program including design verification capability for the personal computer. MyAnalog Station provides a schematic entry with SPICE netlist generation and SPICE simulator. This PC-based tool set is a perfect fit for college students because the tool sets and database are easy to manage and students can work from their individual PCs. The Labs in this book are designed so that the students exercise the lessons they learn from class using MyCAD EDA tool sets.

A successful CMOS VLSI design engineer has knowledge in the areas of device operations, circuit design, layout, and simulation. Students learning CMOS IC design should be trained at a fundamental level in these areas. As transistor feature sizes move towards 0.1 micron, layouts must now be thoroughly considered in the design process because matching and parasitic effects become the limiting factors in many precision and high speed applications. This book evolved from the lecture and Lab notes used since 2000 for teaching the VLSI design class at Northeastern University (ECE1230: VLSI System Design Laboratory) taken by undergraduate students. This book assumes that the readers have a basic understanding of Boolean algebra and fundamental concepts of electrons and holes. At Northeastern University, the VLSI lab class is taken concurrently with the VLSI lecture class (ECE1351). The Labs have been designed so that students can exercise the concepts they learn in the lecture class using MyChip Station. A total of eight Labs have been designed and included in this book. Students are expected to finish one Lab within a week for the first few Labs, and they are expected to finish each Lab within a couple of weeks for the remaining Labs.

This book and these Labs have been designed for one semester courses. The book begins in Chapter 1 with a brief history of IC Design. This chapter introduces the reader to the overall integrated circuit design flow. CMOS fabrication and layout processes are explained in Chapter 2. In addition to the processes, layout examples and layout pitfalls are demonstrated with the first Lab. The students will then create a basic layout using MyCAD tool, and perform RC modeling and SPICE simulation of a simple CMOS transistor structure. In Chapter 3, logic schematic fundamentals are addressed including how to design and create logic schematics. The following will be to design and simulate a D Flip-Flop. Chapter 4 then explores VLSI design styles and Computer-Aided-Design (CAD) tools to give students an idea of what tools are commercially available for different design tasks. Students can explore the hierarchical design and simulation process of a four bit ripple carry adder with the Lab attached to chapter 4. Chapter 5 introduces different layout design styles from standard cell to other varieties of layout such as datapath layout, I/O cell layout, and SRAM cell layout. The Lab in this chapter provides an opportunity to build the four bit ripple carry adder without using library cells. This Lab will help students understand standard cell design and macro cell design processes. In Chapter 6, fundamentals of routing techniques and algorithms are introduced to give students an insight about critical signal routings and CAD tool algorithms. At this point, students need to know how to design and layout non standard type gates. Creating various XOR gate implementations using dynamic gate and pass transistor logic is assigned as a Lab. Chapter 7 covers more detailed layout considerations that minimize the parasitic effects such as latch-up, Electro-Migration (EM), crosstalk, interconnect delay, and strategy for design change. A simple state machine design is assigned as a Lab to exercise MyVHDL and MyLogic Stations. In Chapter 8, global issues such as full chip layout and verification are addressed including a Lab to learn detailed circuit simulation techniques using MyAnalog schematic editor, MySPICE, and Mypostprocessor. In the last chapter, students will learn how to construct design directories and how to manage design data, and the commercially available CAD tools are introduced. An analog circuit design lab is assigned so that students can exercise all the given tools and knowledge they learned from the class.

I am not claiming any of the techniques presented herein as original. Rather, I have gathered these together and combined them with my knowledge and experiences into a single volume. This book grew out of a perceived need in the classroom, the participations and feedback from students, and the encouragement of colleagues. It is a pleasure to acknowledge the contributions of the students who contributed to its generation. I am particularly grateful to graduate assistant Dae Woon Kang for his patience with the ever-changing deadlines and many insightful conversations with students regarding the learning process. I am also grateful to those colleagues who were generous with their time in reading early drafts of the manuscript and forthcoming with their comments and suggestions.

I would like to thank MyCAD, Inc. in general for the support and encouragement they provided throughout the publication process.

Yong-Bin Kim

▌*About the Author*

Dr. Yong-Bin Kim is a professor at Northeastern University and expert in VLSI chip design. Before he joined the Northeastern University, he was a professor at Electrical and Computer Engineering Department of the University of Utah at Salt Lake City, Utah from September 1998 to August 2000.

Professor Kim received the B.S. degree in electrical engineering from Sogang University in Seoul, Korea, and the M.S. and Ph.D. all in computer engineering from New Jersey Institute of Technology and Colorado State University, respectively.

Professor Kim was involved in the state-of-the-art high speed, high performance integrated circuits (VLSI systems) design at Intel Corp., Hewlett Packard Co., SUN Microsystems, and Korean National Research Institute for about 15 years. Professor. Kim participated in the Intel Pentium Pro Microprocessor design as a senior design engineer, HP PA RISC 8000 microprocessor design as a member of technical staff, and 1.5GHz SUN Ultra Sparc CPU Microprocessor design as a staff engineer. And he worked with Electronics and Telecommunications Research Institute in Korea as a member of technical staff, where he participated in analog consumer electronics and mixed mode communications chip design projects.

Professor Kim published more than 30 papers in VLSI design research area, and he understands the critical issues of low power and high performance VLSI design and methodology. Professor Kim's research interests are High speed digital/analog integrated circuit design, high speed integrated circuit signal integrity and physical CAD tool development, IP block design for ASIC, low power and high speed circuit design methodology and technology, high speed system integrations for signal processing and communications applications, innovative circuits and system application.

Program Download
You can download MyCAD software at http://www.mycad.com

$\boldsymbol{C}$ ontents

Chapter I. Introduction

| 1.1 | Historical Perspective of IC Design |

As semiconductor materials and processing technologies have advanced, electronic components have become smaller, circuit arrays denser, microchips larger, and their functions faster and more complex. From the time of its invention in 1948, the bipolar transistor had been the choice for high-performance operation. However, the power dissipated from bipolar circuits could not be decreased as rapidly as the performance of bipolar transistors increased. As linear dimensions reached the half-micron level in the early 1990s, the performance advantage of bipolar transistors was outweighed by the significantly greater circuit density of CMOS circuits using field-effect transistors.

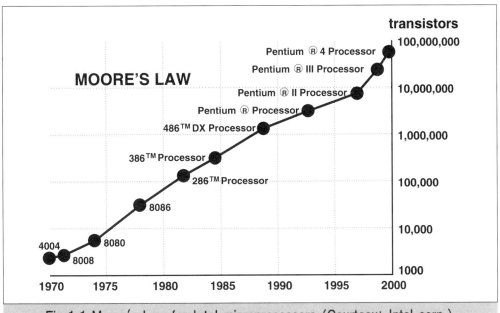

Fig.1.1 Moore's Law for Intel microprocessors (Courtesy: Intel corp.).

Integration refers to the number of transistors placed on a single microchip. The most common description of the evolution of CMOS technology integration is known as Moore's law [MOO] as shown in Fig.1.1. In 1965, Intel Corp. cofounder Gordon Moore predicted that the density of transistors in an integrated circuit would double every year due to improvement in lithographic resolution, and larger chip sizes made possible by enhanced manufacturing techniques and advanced techniques for forming the components on a chip. Integrated circuits are often classified by the number of transistors and other electronic components:

First Transistor (1948) Bell Labs
> 1947 The point-contact bipolar transistor is invented by Bell Lab's Bardeen, Shockley, and Brattain.
> 1951 Junction field-effect transistor (JFET) is invented.
> 1954 Oxide masking process is developed.

SSI (1960's) Small Scale Integration: ~ 20 gates per chip
> 1960 Metal-Oxide-Silicon (MOS) transistor is invented.
> 1962 Transistor-transistor Logic (TTL) is developed.
> 1963 Complementary Metal Oxide Silicon (CMOS) is invented.

MSI (Late 1960's) Medium Scale Integration: 20~200 gates per chip
> 1968 MOS memory circuits are introduced.

LSI (1970's) Large Scale Integration: 200~5000 gates per chip
> 1970 8-bit MOS calculator chips are introduced, 7 μm chip geometries
> 1971 16-bit Microprocessors are introduced.

VLSI (1980's) Very Large Scale Integration: 5000~ ten's of thousands gates per chip
> 1981 Very High Speed Integration (VHSIC), 1.5 μm chip geometries.
> 1984 0.5 μm chip geometries.

ULSI (1990's) Ultra Large Scale Integration: Over millions of transistors per chip

1997 0.25 μm chip geometries.

The monolithic integration of a large number of functions on a single chip usually provides numerous advantages such as reduced area and power consumption, increased reliability due to improved on-chip interconnects, higher speed due to significantly reduced interconnection length, and significant cost savings. With an increase in design complexity, there also came an increase in design cycle time. As a result, sophisticated computer-aided design (CAD) tools and methodologies have been developed in order to manage the rapidly increasing design complexity and reduce the design time.

1.2 IC Design Flow

The IC design process starts with a given set of requirements. After the development, this initial design is tested against the initial design requirements. When these requirements are not satisfied, the design must be improved. If such improvement is either not possible or too costly, then the requirements must be revised and the IC design process re-starts with the new modified requirements. The failure to properly verify a design in its early phases typically causes significant and expensive re-design at a later stage, which ultimately increases the time-to-market. Thus, the verification of the design plays a very important role in every step.

Fig.1.2 provides a view of the Very large scale integration (VLSI) design flow based on schematic capture systems. Although the design process has been described in a linear fashion for simplicity, in reality there are many iterations back and forth, especially between any two neighboring steps, and occasionally even remotely separated pairs. Although top-down design flow provides an excellent design process control, in reality, there is no truly unidirectional top-down design flow. Both top-down and bottom-up approaches have to be combined. For instance, if a chip designer defined an architecture without close estimation of the corresponding chip area, then it is very likely that the resulting chip layout will exceed the area limit of the available technology. In such a case, in order to fit the architecture into the allowable chip area, some functions may have to be removed and the design process must be repeated. Such changes may require significant modification of the initial requirements. Thus, it is very important to feed forward low-level information to higher levels (bottom up) as early as possible.

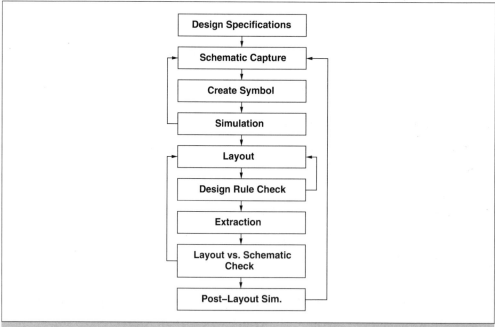

Fig.1.2 A view of VLSI design flow on schematic capture systems.

■ Design Specifications

The bottom-up design flow for a transistor-level circuit layout always starts with a set of design specifications. The "specs" typically describe the expected functionality (Boolean operations) of the designed block, as well as limits on delay times, silicon area and other properties such as power dissipation. Usually, the design specifications allow considerable freedom to the circuit designer on issues concerning the choice of a specific circuit topology, individual placement of the devices, the locations of input and output pins, and the overall aspect ratio (width-to-height ratio) of the final design. Note that the limitations spelled out in the initial design specs typically require certain design trade-offs, such as increasing the dimensions of the transistors in order to reduce the delay times. It can be seen that one can design a number of different adders (with different topologies, different maximum delays, different total silicon areas, etc.), all of which essentially conform to the specs listed above. This indicates that the starting point of a typical bottom-up design process usually leaves the designer a considerable amount of design freedom.

■ Schematic Capture

The traditional method for capturing a transistor-level or gate-level design is via a schematic editor. Schematic editors provide simple, intuitive means to draw, place and connect individual components that make up a design. The resulting schematic drawing must accurately describe the main electrical properties of all components and their interconnections. Also included in the schematic are the power supply and ground connections, as well as all pins for the input/output interface of the circuit. This information is crucial for generating the corresponding netlist, which is used in later stages of the design. The generation of a complete circuit schematic is therefore the first important step of the transistor-level design flow. Usually, some properties of the components and/or the interconnections between the devices are subsequently modified as a result of iterative optimization steps.

■ Symbol Creation

If a certain circuit design consists of smaller hierarchical components, it is usually very beneficial to identify such modules early in the design process and to assign each module a corresponding symbol to represent that circuit. This step greatly simplifies the schematic representation of the overall system. The symbol view of a circuit module is an icon that represents the collection of all components within the module. A symbol view of the circuit is also required for some of the subsequent simulation steps; therefore the schematic capture of the circuit topology is usually followed by the creation of a symbol to represent the entire circuit.

■ Simulation

After the transistor-level description of a circuit is completed using the Schematic Editor, the electrical performance and the functionality of the circuit must be verified using a Simulation tool. The detailed transistor-level simulation of a design will be the first in-depth validation of its operation, and it is therefore extremely important to complete this step before proceeding to the subsequent design optimization steps. Based on simulation results, the designer usually modifies some of the device properties in order to optimize the performance. The initial simulation phase also serves in detecting possible design errors that may have been created during the schematic entry step. It is quite common to discover errors such as a missing connection or an extra connection (an unintended crossing of two signals) in the schematic. The second simulation phase follows the extraction of a mask layout to accurately assess the electrical performance of the completed design.

■ Layout

The creation of the mask layout is one of the most important steps in the full-custom (bottom-up) design flow. This is where the designer describes the detailed geometries and the relative positioning of each mask layer to be used in actual fabrication, using a Layout Editor. Physical layout design is very tightly linked to overall circuit performance (area, speed and power dissipation) since the physical structure determines the transconductances of the transistors, the parasitic capacitances and resistances, and obviously, the silicon area which is used to realize a certain function. On the other hand, the detailed mask layout of logic gates requires a very intensive and time-consuming design effort. The physical design of CMOS logic gates is an iterative process which starts with the circuit topology and the initial sizing of the transistors.

■ Design Rule Check (DRC)

The created mask layout must conform to a complex set of design rules, in order to ensure a lower probability of fabrication defects. A tool built into the Layout Editor, called Design Rule Checker, is used to detect any design rule violations during and after the mask layout design. The designer must perform DRC, and make sure that all errors are eventually removed from the mask layout, before the final design is saved.

▣ Circuit Extraction

Circuit extraction is performed after the mask layout design is completed in order to create a detailed netlist for the simulation tool. The circuit extractor is capable of identifying the individual transistors and their interconnections as well as the parasitic resistances and capacitances that are inevitably present between these layers. The extracted netlist can provide a very accurate estimation of the actual device dimensions and device parasitics that ultimately determine circuit performance. The extracted netlist file and parameters are subsequently used in Layout-Versus-Schematic comparison and in detailed transistor-level simulations (post-layout simulation).

▣ Layout Versus Schematic (LVS) Check

After the mask layout design of the circuit is completed, the design should be checked against the schematic circuit description created earlier. By comparing the original network with the one extracted from the mask layout the designer can check that the two networks are indeed equivalent. The LVS step provides an additional level of confidence for the integrity of the design, and ensures that the mask layout is a correct realization of the intended circuit topology. Note that the LVS check only guarantees a topological match. In other words, a successful LVS will not guarantee that the extracted circuit will actually satisfy the performance requirements. Any errors that may show up during LVS such as unintended connections between transistors, or missing connections/devices, etc. should be corrected in the mask layout – before proceeding to post-layout simulation.

▣ Post-layout Simulation

The electrical performance of a full-custom design can be best analyzed by performing a post-layout simulation on the extracted circuit netlist. At this point, the designer should have a complete mask layout of the intended circuit/system, and should have passed the DRC and LVS steps with no violations. The detailed (transistor-level) simulation performed using the extracted netlist will provide a clear assessment of the circuit speed, the influence of circuit parasitics such as parasitic capacitances and resistances, and any glitches that may occur due to signal delay mismatches. If the results of post-layout simulation are not satisfactory, the designer should modify some of the transistor dimensions and/or the circuit topology, in order to achieve the desired circuit performance under realistic conditions. This may require multiple iterations on the design until the post-layout simulation results satisfy the original design requirements. However, a satisfactory result in post-layout simulation is still no guarantee for a completely successful product; the actual performance of the chip can only be verified by testing the fabricated prototype.

1.3 Detailed Physical Design Cycle

The physical design stage transforms circuit design specifications into physical mask representations used to manufacture the electronic circuit. The designer must follow strict geometric design rules associated with the constraints of the fabrication process. These include requirements for minimum feature sizes of the various components, as well as the spacings and connections between them. Failure to follow these rules can make the chip inoperable, unreliable, or unmanufacturable. Physical design is iterative in nature and many steps are repeated several times in order to obtain a better layout. In addition, the quality of results obtained in a step depends on the quality of the solutions obtained in earlier steps. In general, the whole design cycle may be repeated several times to accomplish the design objectives. Fig.1.3 shows the sequence of physical design.

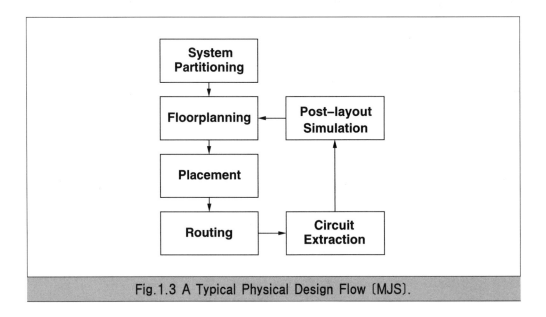

Fig.1.3 A Typical Physical Design Flow [MJS].

■ Partitioning Step

A chip may contain several million transistors. The layout of the whole chip cannot be handled due to the limitation of memory space, as well as computation time. Therefore, it is normally partitioned by grouping components into blocks as shown in Fig.1.4. The actual partitioning process considers many factors such as the size of the blocks, the number of blocks, and the number of interconnections between the blocks. The output of partitioning is a set of blocks along with the interconnections required between blocks. In large circuits, the partitioning process is hierarchical and at the top-most level a chip may have between 5 to 25 blocks. Each module is then partitioned recursively into smaller blocks.

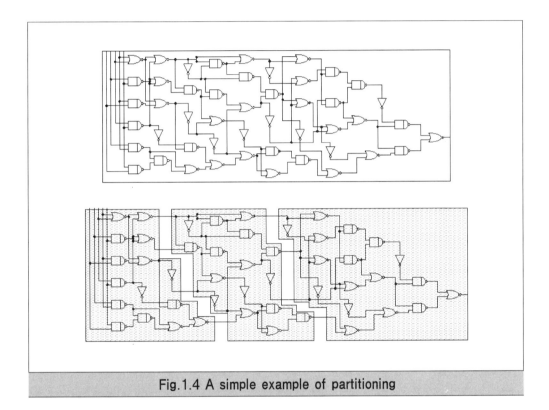

Fig.1.4 A simple example of partitioning

▣ Floor−planning and Placement Step

This step is concerned with selecting good layout alternatives for each block as well as the entire chip. The area of each block can be calculated after partitioning and is based approximately on the number and the type of components in that block. The actual rectangular shape of the block, which is determined by the aspect ratio, may vary within a pre-specified range. In executing a complex layout, it is worthwhile to develop a plan for how the various subcells are to be placed and connected. This process is generally referred to as floorplanning. A well-done floorplan greatly minimizes area and routing complexity and can even simplify subcell layout. Thus, very often, the task of floor-plan layout is done by a design engineer, rather than by a CAD tool. This is sometimes necessary as the major components of an IC are often intended for specific locations on the chip.

A critical part of floorplanning is decided which signals travel in which tracks and how far. Since it is assumed that a track passes completely over any leaf cell without interference, the importance of not using the upper metal layers within the subcells should be obvious. Exceptions occur only when the subcell actually needs to connect to that track. In other words, a cell that does not connect to any tracks should not have any metal drawn in them; the tracks passing over that cell are drawn on the top level of the layout. When a leaf cell connects to a track, the track may be filled from the use of the signal to the edge(s) of the cell in the direction(s) that the signal needs to travel.

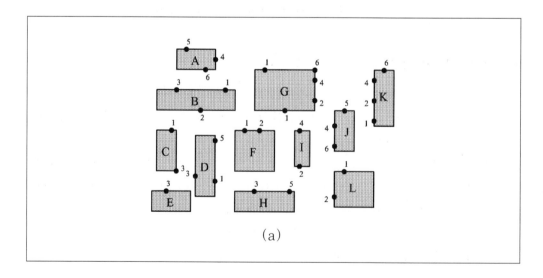

(a)

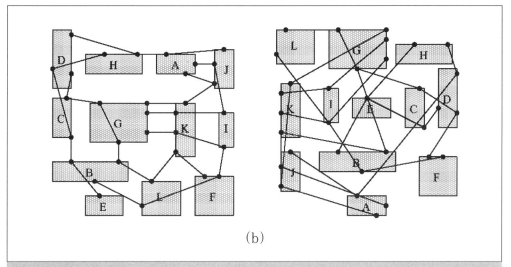

(b)

Fig.1.5 (a) A group of blocks under placement, and (b) two examples of placement.

Note that the same track can correspond to different signals at either end of the cell. Higher metal layers are sometimes needed for some local routing within the cells. In such a case, one should try to minimize the number of tracks used to avoid interference with top level signals. Do not forget to allocate tracks across every cell for VDD and GND

During **placement**, the blocks are exactly positioned on the chip. As shown in Fig.1.5, the goal of placement is to find a minimum area arrangement for the blocks that allows completion of interconnections between the blocks. Placement is typically done in two phases. In the first phase, an initial placement is created. In the second phase, the initial placement is evaluated and iterative improvements are made until the layout has minimum area and conforms to design specifications. Between adjacent cells, interconnection is as simple as ensuring that the signal in each cell goes all the way to the edge of the cell at the same location on the common edge. In this way, the mere placement of the cells adjacent to each other in the next level of layout hierarchy connects the two cells properly. This eliminates the need to manually connect adjacent cells on the top level and helps to guide the layout of the leaf cells. However, it also requires that the leaf cell layouts meet design rule requirements when placed adjacent to each other.

The quality of the placement will not be evident until the routing phase has been completed. Placement may lead to an un-routable design, i.e., routing may not be possible in the space provided. In that case, another iteration of placement is necessary. To limit the number of iterations of the placement algorithm, an estimate of the required routing space is used during the placement phase. Good routing and circuit performance heavily depend on a good placement algorithm. This is due to the fact that once the position of each block is fixed, very little can be done to improve the routing and the overall circuit performance.

■ Routing and Compaction Step

Interconnect design and optimization have received much attention recently in deep sub-micron VLSI layout design. The objective of the routing phase is to complete the interconnections between blocks according to the specified netlist. First, the space not occupied by the blocks (called the routing space) is partitioned into rectangular regions called channels and switchboxes. The goal of a router is to complete all circuit connections using the shortest possible wire length and using only the channel and switch boxes. This is usually done in two phases, referred to as the global and detailed routing phases.

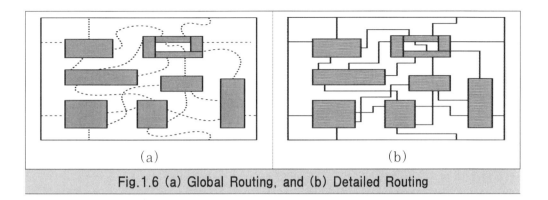

Fig.1.6 (a) Global Routing, and (b) Detailed Routing

Global routing is often planned with the aid of these channels and tracks. Channels are areas of a die between functional units used exclusively for routing. They are often highly oblong to accommodate long buses. Because most metal layers in a channel are used for routing, it is usually not possible to put devices into the channels. Routing tracks are used to organize and simplify routing within and over layout cells. Generally, global routing layers (the higher metal layers) are assigned a preferred direction that alternates every layer. Usually this direction restriction does not apply to the lowest one or two metal layers because of their use in convoluted local routes. Picture the entire layout overlaid with minimum width metal lines running the length of the bit slice. The lines are at the minimum pitch which allows space for via landing pads to upper and lower metal layers. Each of these hypothetical metal lines is referred to as a track. Global routing is followed by **detailed routing**, which completes point-to-point connections between pins on the blocks. Loose routing is converted into exact routing by specifying geometric information such as width of wires and their layer assignments.

Compaction is simply the task of compressing the layout in all directions such that the total area is reduced. By making the chip smaller, wire lengths are reduced which in turn reduces the signal delay between components of the circuit. At the same time, this reduced area implies that more chips can be produced on a single wafer driving down the cost of manufacturing. Compaction must ensure that no rules regarding the design and fabrication process are violated during the process.

■ Extraction

Circuit extractors analyze the layout and extract a netlist of transistors, thus converting a physical description back to a structural description. The structural circuit description can then be simulated with a switch or circuit simulator. Programs to verify the extracted netlist include: a network comparison program, which compares the netlist from the circuit design phase to the extracted netlist from the physical design; and an electrical rules checker (ERC), which checks the electrical properties of a circuit. Parameter extractors can determine electrical parameters from layout information for timing simulation.

■ Post-Layout Simulation

Finally, post-layout simulation ensures that the chosen design performs all the desired functions with extracted parameters. This simulation also helps determine the circuit's operating speed and checks any delays accurately.

References

[MOO] Gordon E. Moore, "Cramming More Components onto Integrated Circuits," *Electronics. Vol.*38, April 19, 1965.
[MJS] Michael John Sebastian and John Smith, *Application-Specific Integrated Circuits*, Wesley Publishing Company, 1997.

Pre-Lab1: IC Layout

MyChip is an interactive system for creating and modifying VLSI circuit layouts. With MyChip, you use a color graphics display and a mouse to design basic cells and to combine them hierarchically into larger structures. MyChip has built-in DRC program – when you are running, DRC checks for design rule violations. MyChip must be run from a PC that supports the Windows system.

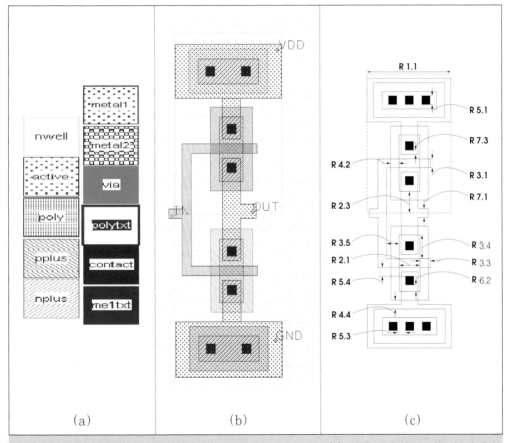

(a)   (b)   (c)

Fig.P1.1 (a) Legend of colors (b) an example of an inverter (c) applied design rules for Lab1.

MyChip can use both "lambda-based" design rule and "micron-based" design rule. In scalable ("lambda-based") design, layout items are aligned to a grid which represents a basic unit of space. The drawing window is a layout surface on which items can be placed with a resolution of one lambda. In this lab, the given DRC rule is based on lambda rule, and one lambda is 0.5um. While drawing an inverter, however, your feature sizes are shown in micrometers in the MyChip Layout Editor.

In MyChip, a circuit layout is a hierarchical collection of cells. Each cell contains three things: colored shapes called paint, that define the circuit's structure; textual labels attached to the paint; and subcells, which are instances of other cells. Fig.P1.1 shows a legend of relevant colors/layers and a layout example of an inverter. Some layers are created by crossing two layers. For example, drawing poly over active (or vice versa) will produce a transistor.

▣ Drawing Layer Definition:

Table. P1.1 Layers of the given technology for Lab1.

Name of layer	What the layer represents
Nwell	nwell
Active	active
Poly	polysilicon
Pplus	*active and pplus → p-diffusion (p+source/drain areas)*
Nplus	*active and nplus → n-diffusion (n+source/drain areas)*
metal1	*metal1*
metal2	*metal2*
Via	*Metal1 and metal2 contact*
Polytxt	poly text
Contact	*Metal1 to diffusion contact*
me1txt	metal1 text

■ Parasitic Layer Definition:

NOT	pbulk nwell	$\rightarrow$ psub
AND	active pplus	$\rightarrow$ pactive
AND	active nplus	$\rightarrow$ nactive
AND	pactive poly	$\rightarrow$ pgate
AND	nactive poly	$\rightarrow$ ngate
NOT	pactive poly	$\rightarrow$ psd
NOT	nactive poly	$\rightarrow$ nsd
AND	nwell nactive	$\rightarrow$ nplug
AND	psub pactive	$\rightarrow$ pplug
AND	pplug contact	$\rightarrow$ ppcont
AND	nplug contact	$\rightarrow$ npcont

■ Design Rule for Lab1:

n-well (Lambda base)

Rule 1.1:	width (n-well)	⟨ 10
Rule 1.2:	space (n-well) diff voltage	⟨ 9
Rule 1.3:	space (n-well) same voltage	⟨ 6

active (Lambda base)

Rule 2.1:	width (active)	⟨ 3
Rule 2.2:	space (active)	⟨ 3
Rule 2.3:	well edge enclose (pactive)	⟨ 5
Rule 2.4:	well edge space (nacitve)	⟨ 5
Rule 2.5:	well contact (/active) space (nplug)	⟨ 3
Rule 2.6:	well contact (/active) space (pplug)	⟨ 3
Rule 2.7:	space (nactive, pactive)	⟨ 4

poly (Lambda base)

Rule 3.1:	width (poly)	⟨ 2
Rule 3.2:	space (poly)	⟨ 2
Rule 3.3:	min gate extension of active	⟨ 2
Rule 3.4:	min active extension of poly from nactive	⟨ 3
Rule 3.5:	min active extension of poly from pactive	⟨ 3
Rule 3.6:	min field poly to active	⟨ 3

select (Lambda base)

Rule 4.1:	min select spacing to channel, space (ngate, pplus)	⟨ 3
Rule 4.2:	min select spacing to channel, space (pgate, nplus)	⟨ 3
Rule 4.3:	min select overlap of active, overlap (pplus, active)	⟨ 2
Rule 4.4:	min select overlap of active, overlap (nplus, active)	⟨ 2
Rule 4.5:	min select overlap of contact, overlap (pplus, contact)	⟨ 1
Rule 4.6:	min select overlap of contact, overlap (nplus, contact)	⟨ 1
Rule 4.7:	min p+ select width	⟨ 2
Rule 4.8:	min n+ select width	⟨ 2
Rule 4.9:	min p+ select space	⟨ 2
Rule 4.10:	min n+ select space	⟨ 2
Rule 4.11:	min space (between n+ and p+ select)	⟨ 2

simple contact to poly (Lambda base)

Rule 5.1:	exact contact size	⟨ 2
Rule 5.2:	minimum poly overlap of contact	⟨ 1.5
Rule 5.3:	space (contact)	⟨ 2
Rule 5.4:	space (contact, pgate)	⟨ 2
Rule 5.5:	space (contact, ngate)	⟨ 2

simple contact to active (Lambda base)

Rule 6.1:	min active overlap of contact	⟨ 1.5

metal1 (Lambda base)

Rule 7.1:	width (metal1)	〈 3
Rule 7.2:	space (metal1)	〈 3
Rule 7.3:	min metal1 overlap of contact, enclose (metal1, contact)	〈 1

via (Lambda base)

Rule 8.1:	exact via size	〈 2
Rule 8.2:	via space	〈 3
Rule 8.3:	min metal1 overlap of via, enclose (metal1,via)	〈 1
Rule 8.4:	min space (via, contact)	〈 2
Rule 8.5:	min space (via, poly)	〈 2
Rule 8.6:	min space (via, active)	〈 2

metal2 (Lambda base)

Rule 9.1:	min width (metal2)	〈 3
Rule 9.2:	min space (metal2)	〈 4
Rule 9.3:	min metal2 overlap of via, enclose (metal2, via)	〈 1

Layout of a CMOS Inverter

Here is a step by step example of how to layout a CMOS logic inverter (Fig.P1.1 (b)). The inverter consists of one NMOS transistor and one PMOS transistor. The channel width W and the channel length L of the two devices are indicated in μm. Note that the source and the body (p-substrate) of the NMOS are connected to ground (GND node), while the source and the body (nwell) of the PMOS are connected to the positive supply (VDD node). In this example, we use basic MyChip drawing commands to layout the inverter. Since the device channel width W and length L are specified, we can start by painting the device active areas: p-diffusion for PMOS and n-diffusion for NMOS. The order in which layers are placed in the graphics window is not important, and so the layout steps described here are by no means unique.

ⓐ The PMOS transistor has the channel width W=12λ and the channel length L=6λ. According to the given design rules (Fig.P1.1(c)), make a box - 12λ wide (design spec) and 26 λ high (2(R 4.5: source overlap of contact) + 4(R 5.1: source contact size) + 4(R 5.3: space to poly) + 6(design spec: channel length) + 4(R 5.3: space to poly) + 4(R 5.1: drain contact size) + 2(R 4.5: drain overlap of contact)), as shown in the figure below. Make the PMOS active area (p-diffusion) which consists of overlap area of active and p+ layers (Fig.P1.2).

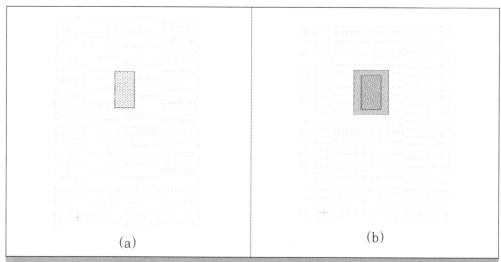

(a)

(b)

Fig.P1.2 (a) Active layer and (b) active and p+ layers (p-diffusion).

ⓑ Paint the NMOS active area (n-diffusion) like we made the PMOS. The NMOS transistor has the channel width W=12λ, and the channel length L=6λ. Make a 12λ (width) by 26λ (height) box under the p-diffusion area you already painted. Make the NMOS active area (n-diffusion) which consists of overlap area of active and n+ layers. A design rule is that n+ must be at least 4λ away from pplus. (Fig.P1.3).

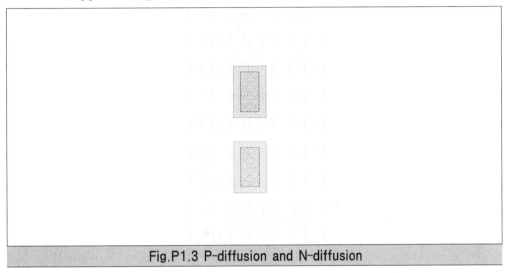

Fig.P1.3 P-diffusion and N-diffusion

ⓒ Next, paint horizontally metal1 wires minimum 16λ that will serve as VDD and GND.

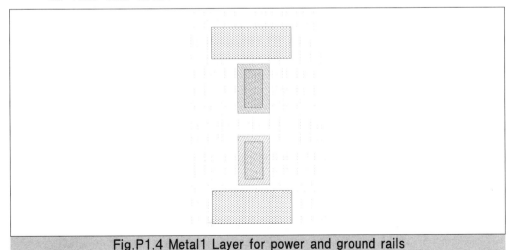

Fig.P1.4 Metal1 Layer for power and ground rails

CMOS VLSI Layout Artwork Design and Lab ·····································

ⓓ The next step is to paint the nwell area where the PMOS is located. Place a box extending at least 10λ above and below the pactive, and as wide as the metal1 wires.

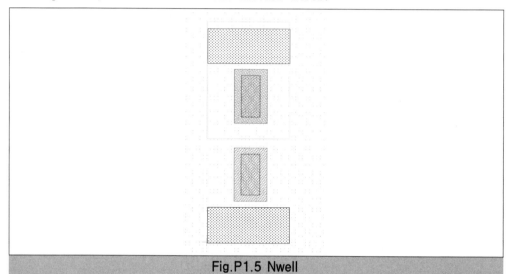

Fig.P1.5 Nwell

ⓔ Then, connect the sources of the NMOS and the PMOS to Power and Ground Rails respectively. Layout the output node using metal1 and make drain contacts. (Fig.P1.6).

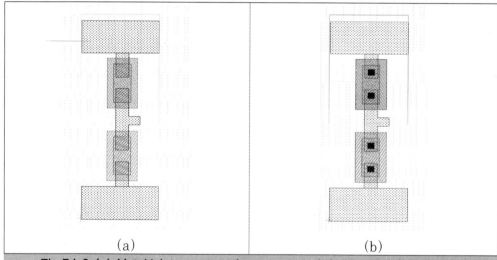

(a)   (b)

Fig.P1.6 (a) Metal1 interconnect for source and drain and (b) contacts.

❺ The next step is to paint the gates of the NMOS and the PMOS. Connect the poly areas of both gates and make the input node (Fig.P1.7).

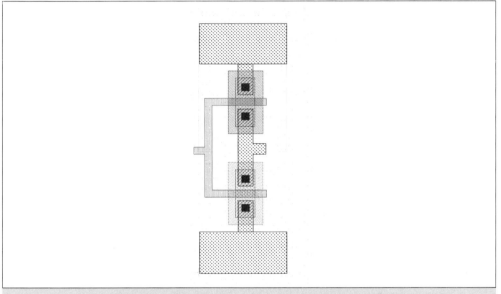

Fig.P1.7 Poly Layer for gate interconnect

❻ At this point, we can add contacts between the GND wire and the p-substrate (body of the NMOS), as well as between the VDD wire and the n-well (body of the PMOS). Place a 4λ by 4λ box over the center of power wire (metal1), but do not overlap the PMOS source contact you already made (Fig.P1.6). The body contacts should always be located as close as possible to the device source contacts to minimize the possibility of latch-up that plagues CMOS circuits. It is also good practice to put as many body contacts as possible. The next steps are the same as the steps you used to create the source contacts (Fig.P1.8) except of p+ and n+ layers. In other words, n+ layer is needed for VDD bulk contact and n+ layer is used for GND bulk contact.

ⓗ Then, in order to make your layout readable, and to prepare your layout for extraction and simulation, you need to label input/output and power ports (See Fig.P1.1 (b)). You should see a small yellow + at that spot. Label the input node of the inverter as in. Similarly, label the VDD-wire as VDD, the GND-wire as GND, and the output wire as out. Label names can be anything, but it is a good idea to use the labels that will correspond to circuit signals and make the layout readable.

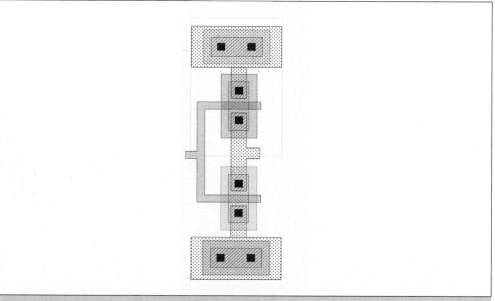

Fig.P1.8 Nwell contact (contact + active + n+) and P-substrate contact layers (contact + active + p+).

ⓘ Design Rule Check is a built-in feature of MyChip. In general, design rules specify how far apart various layers must be, or how large various aspects of the layout must be for successful fabrication, given the tolerances and other limitations of the fabrication process. Any time you place wires too close together, paint a block too narrow, or make any other rule violations,

MyChip lets you know by running the DRC tool.

● The built-in MyChip extractor generates from the layout the netlist needed to run simulation tool-MySPICE. The netlist includes the sizes and shapes of the transistors, and the connectivity, resistance, and parasitic capacitances of the nodes.

Chapter II. CMOS Fabrication and Layout Processes

Integrated circuits(IC) eliminated the many discrete electronic components that make up a hard-wired circuit (including resistors, inductors, and capacitors). Instead, semiconductor materials such as silicon and germanium now do the work of these individual components. Because they are smaller, more reliable, cost less, and perform better than conventional circuits, semiconductor integrated circuits are now the basic components of today's electronic systems. There are several different types of semiconductors, which vary in terms of how the transistors are made out of silicon. The differences between them are highly technical so they will not be explained in detail here. The earliest Integrated Circuits were manufactured using bipolar technology such as transistor-transistor logic (TTL) and emitter-coupled logic (ECL). However, Complementary Metal Oxide Semiconductor (CMOS) has been the dominant semiconductor technology for microprocessors, memories and application specific integrated circuits (ASIC). The main advantage of CMOS over other technologies is the much smaller power dissipation. Unlike bipolar circuits, a CMOS circuit has almost no static power dissipation. Power is only dissipated when the circuit actually performs switching.

Extremely pure silicon is used as a base semiconductor material for integrated circuits. By doping silicon with phosphorus, the silicon acquires excess electrons and is called n-type silicon. Doped with boron, the silicon has a lack of electrons and is called p-type silicon. CMOS fabrication technology requires that both n-channel (NMOS) and p-channel (PMOS) transistors be built on the same chip substrate. Single process steps are combined to a complete process flow with a few hundred steps for a typical CMOS process. Since any structure on the chip depends on many of the process steps there is a strong interdependence between the various steps. As shown in Fig.2.1, the main techniques to create the desired topography on the wafer are thermal oxidation of silicon, lithography, etching and deposition processes, conventional and selective epitaxial growth, viscous flow of deposited glasses (CVD oxides), formation of silicides, and chemical-mechanical polishing.

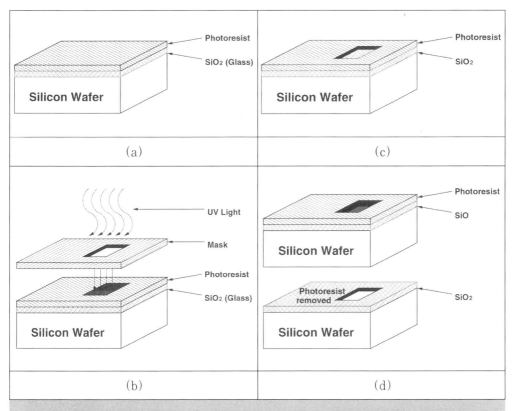

Fig.2.1 MOS topography technology: (a) Acid resistant coating (photoresist) spread evenly on surface, (b) Polymerized in areas exposed by UV light, (c) Organic solvent removes polymerized areas, and (d) Windows are etched using an acid and the photoresist is removed [WAE].

2.1 MOS Switch

A MOS transistor is a voltage-controlled switch. It has four connection points: a source, a drain, a gate, and a substrate. Fig.2.2 shows in a cross section of the n-type metal-oxide-silicon (NMOS) transistor. The basic MOS transistor configuration consists of silicon on the bottom layer and metal on the top layer with an insulating oxide layer sandwiched in between. The source and drain regions contain silicon material with a large excess of electrons separated by the slightly positively charged bulk silicon. The source and drain are called diffusion regions because of the chemical process used to create them. Negatively charged ions (atoms with extra valence electrons) are placed onto the silicon surface and are diffused into the surface by heating the silicon material. The materials of the source and drain are identical. By convention, the source in NMOS is the electrical node with the lower of the two voltage potentials at either end of the channel.

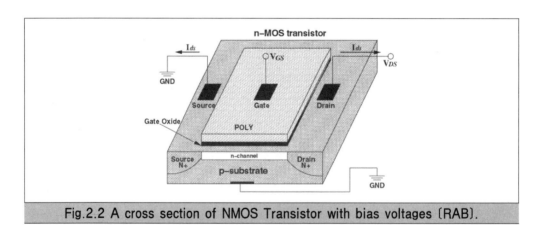

Fig.2.2 A cross section of NMOS Transistor with bias voltages (RAB).

The electrical behavior of the transistor is generally as follows. When a positive voltage is placed on the gate, electrons from the silicon bulk are attracted to the transistor channel. The channel, initially, is a non-conducting region between the source and drain very close to the silicon surface. When the gate voltage becomes sufficiently positively charged ($V_{GS} > V_t$), enough electrons are pulled into the channel from the bulk to establish a charged path between the source and the drain. Electrons flow across the transistor channel, and the voltage-controlled switch is conducting. If a ʹ0ʹ or very small voltage ($V_{GS} < V_t$) is placed on the gate, electrons are not attracted to the channel. The source and drain are disconnected, no current flows across the channel, and the switch is not conducting. As shown in Fig.2.3, the MOS transistor has three major regions of operation: cutoff, saturation and non-saturated (triode) region. In the triode region, the voltage drop across the drain-source terminals approaches zero volts, and the magnitude of the voltage drop across the gate-source terminals approaches VDD – VSS. In the cutoff region, the drain-to-source current, I_{DS}, approaches zero amps. Hence, the drain and source terminals of a MOS transistor can be treated as an ideal switch alternating between the ʺoffʺ and ʺonʺ modes of operation.

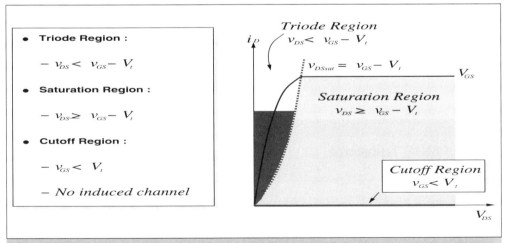

- **Triode Region :**
    - $v_{DS} < v_{GS} - V_t$
- **Saturation Region :**
    - $v_{DS} \geq v_{GS} - V_t$
- **Cutoff Region :**
    - $v_{GS} < V_t$
    - *No induced channel*

Fig.2.3 Regions of operation for NMOS Transistor according to V_DS and V_GS (RAB).

There are two fundamentally different kinds of MOS transistors, called n-channel and p-channel transistors, or NMOS and PMOS for short. Because they are made from materials with different affinities for electrons, the two transistor types behave quite differently. The transistor operation described above is actually for the NMOS transistor. The bulk is positively charged, while the diffusion is negatively charged. As shown in Fig.2.4, the transistor switch is "on" (conducting) when a logic '1' is placed on its gate and "off" (non-conducting) when the gate is connected to a logic '0'. The PMOS transistor is complementary. The diffusion regions are positively charged and the silicon bulk is negatively charged. A PMOS transistor behaves in a complementary way: It is "on" (conducting) when a logic '0' is placed on the gate and is "off" (non-conducting) when a logic '1' is placed there.

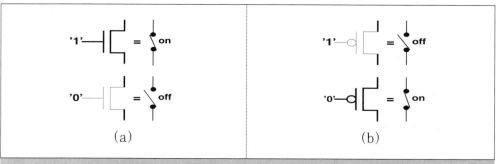

(a)   (b)

Fig.2.4 MOS logic switches: (a) NMOS, and (b) PMOS.

2.2 CMOS Transistor

There is a limitation on the use of the MOS transistors as ideal switches. An NMOS transistor provides a strong '0', but a weak '1'. On the other hand, a PMOS transistor provides a strong '1', but a weak '0'.

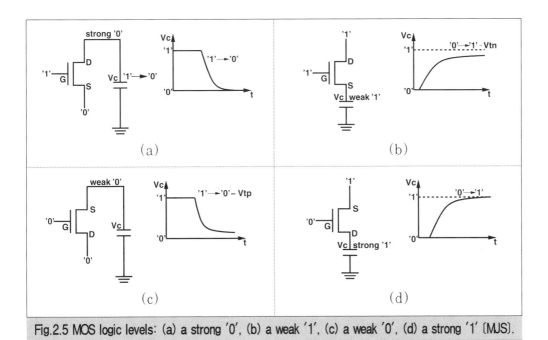

Fig.2.5 MOS logic levels: (a) a strong '0', (b) a weak '1', (c) a weak '0', (d) a strong '1' [MJS].

For proper operation as an ideal switch, the PMOS transistor or network must be connected to the most positive voltage rail while the NMOS transistor or network must be connected to the most negative voltage rail because of the electrical characteristics of NMOS and PMOS (Fig.2.5(a) - (d)). For example, if a logic '1' is applied to the drain as shown in Fig.2.5(b), the NMOS transistor is still on, but V_{GS} is decreasing until the source voltage approaches its final value.

To overcome this limitation of MOS transistors, the Complementary Metal Oxide Semiconductor (CMOS) transistor was invented [SPC]. In CMOS, there is no weak value, thus, the speed of any operation is as fast as the fastest NMOS action. The fundamental building blocks of CMOS circuits are P-type and N-type MOSFET transistors. The simplest CMOS structure is the CMOS inverter, shown in Fig.2.6. This particular inverter is built on a substrate of p-type material, with an n-type well acting as a substrate for the PMOS transistor. These two MOSFETs are completely opposite but with the same function.

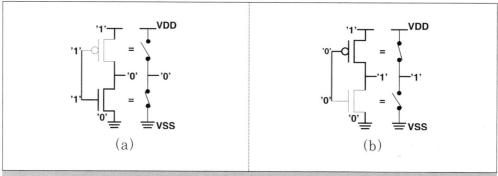

(a) (b)

Fig.2.6 Operations for INVERTER gate according to input states.

In the CMOS inverter, the voltage V_I applied across the gates of both transistors is the same. Thus, a high V_I turns the n-channel device's channel on, and a low V_I turns the p-channel on. VDD is also applied to the source terminal of the p-channel transistor, and its drain is connected to the drain terminal of the NMOS transistor. The NMOS source is then connected to ground. When the input voltage is high, turning the n-channel on, VDD drops mostly across the p-channel, and the output voltage V_O is low. Similarly, when V_I is low (turning the n-channel off but the p-channel on), VDD drops mostly across the n-channel and V_O is high. The reason why CMOS circuits have low power dissipation is that at least one of the transistors is turned off so that there is no conducting path from the supply voltage to ground. As a consequence, CMOS circuits consume very little energy and produce low static power dissipation [MSS]. The main problem of CMOS is that all logic must be duplicated and this uses larger amounts of space. Fortunately, the space costs are not always of major concern and there are dynamic design styles that reduce the area [WAE]. Thus, CMOS is rapidly becoming the most popular integrated-circuit environment.

2.3 CMOS Process

In an N-Well process, as shown in Fig.2.7 (a)-(g), the substrate is P-type and the NMOS transistor is created in the P-type substrate, and the PMOS transistor is created in the N-Well.

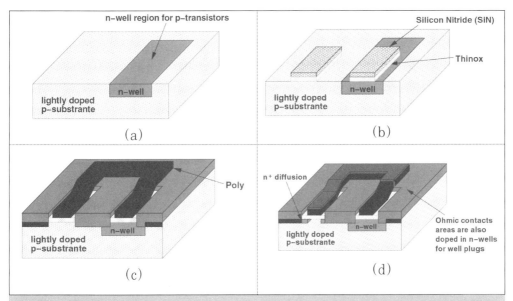

Fig.2.7 CMOS Fabrication Process (N-well): (a) N-well mask used to create n-well or n-tub via ion-implantation or deposition/diffusion, (b) Active mask defines areas where transistors are fabricated, (c) P-well mask used to produce channel-stop (p+ diffusion), field oxide grown, (d) Poly mask used to etch poly patterns, (e) P+ mask used to indicate those thin-oxide areas and poly where p+ is to be implanted, (f) Surface is covered with SiO_2 and contact cuts made, and (g) Metallization applied and etched using metal mask [WAE].

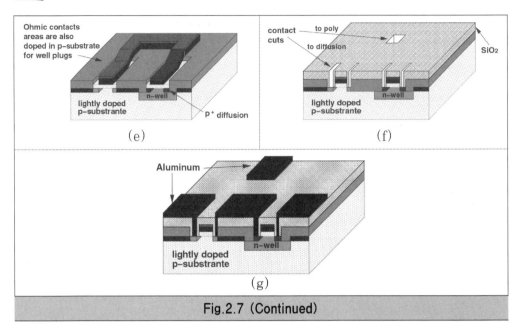

Fig.2.7 (Continued)

The process sequence for the fabrication of CMOS IC starts with the creation of the N-well regions for PMOS transistors. This is done by implanting impurities into the substrate. A thick oxide is then grown in the regions surrounding the NMOS and PMOS active regions. The thin gate oxide is subsequently grown on the surface through thermal oxidation. These steps are followed by the creation of n+ and p+ regions (source, drain and channel-stop implants) then finally metallization (creation of metal interconnects). All the N-wells must be connected to the most positive potential on the chip, normally VDD, and all the p-substrate to VSS to avoid forward biasing the bulk to source/drain PN-junctions. The bulk connections for CMOS transistors are not usually drawn in digital circuit schematics, but these substrate contacts are very important. The following depicts the specific processes of the IC fabrication [SNT].

◼ Implantation

The method of introducing impurities is called implantation. The source of the chosen impurity is placed above the wafer surface. Depending on the type of semiconductor, boron, gallium, or sulphur can be used for the impurity. The impurities are generated as ions. An ion is an atom with some electrons removed, and is therefore positively charged, or with extra electrons and therefore negatively charged. Once generated, the ions are accelerated toward the wafer by putting an extremely high negative voltage across the wafer and the ion source. The positive ions are attracted to the wafer by the negative voltage. Magnets are used to focus and steer the ions. They travel so fast that they literally embed themselves into the surface of the silicon wafer. The higher their speed, the deeper they go. This process is called ion implantation.

◼ Diffusion

Ion implantation may brutally force atoms into the surface, damaging the crystal lattice. Since the PN junctions rely on a good crystal lattice structure to function correctly, the crystal lattice should be reconstructed. To repair the crystal lattice, the wafer is annealed (heated). This helps all atoms loosen and settle with each other, forming a more consistent structure. When annealed, the atoms move in, down, and outward through the silicon just like ink mixing in, down, and outward through water. Although the initial depth of implantation is very shallow, annealing makes the atoms diffuse outward. The implanted atoms spread themselves through the material in all directions. This is called diffusion.

◼ Epitaxial Deposition

Some types of semiconductor devices need very good, thin layers of silicon, one on top of the other, in order to function correctly.

Therefore, any new layers of silicon need to match the substrate crystal lattice. Growing a new layer of silicon on top of another layer of silicon while maintaining the lattice structure, is called epitaxial deposition.

■ Chemical Vapor Deposition

Certain gases mixed at a high temperature will react with one other to produce silicon. By controlling the temperature, the atoms can be condensed on the wafer. Growing a new layer using a mixture of gases is called Chemical Vapor Deposition (CVD).

Whereas epitaxial layers, which are silicon on silicon, are grown slowly to maintain the crystal lattice, silicon is grown quickly using CVD and does not have a very good crystal structure. It is made up of many different crystals that eventually join, rather than being one large crystal. This type of silicon is known as Poly-Crystalline Silicon, or referred to simply as Poly. Poly is used extensively in IC's to make FET Gates and resistors. The doping is usually done to change its resistivity, whereas doping regular silicon is to set energy levels and transistor characteristics.

■ Oxide Growth

It is required to build wiring and other conductive materials over the top of the chip. Isolation of the layers from one other is needed to prevent a short it with another metal layer. An easy way to create a layer of isolation is to stick the wafer in a furnace with oxygen and heat it up. The silicon on the surface turns to silicon dioxide which is a very good insulator.

■ Sputtering

Plasma is a state of matter formed when gases at very low pressures are subjected to high-frequency and high-voltage. High-energy plasma can be used to help deposit materials that cannot be deposited using CVD. Plasma made from inert gas, such as argon, can be used to knock atoms into submission. As the high-energy argon atoms smash into the metal, they force metal atoms to separate from the block, flying out into the plasma. The metal atoms become ionized by their ordeal and are attracted to the safety of the wafers. As the process continues, more metal atoms get blasted away, sticking to the wafer surface. Eventually the wafers are coated with the correct thickness of the metal

■ Evaporation

Another way of depositing metal is called Evaporation. The wafer is loaded into a large chamber that has all the air sucked out of it. This chamber contains a large tungsten filament. The coils of this filament have small chunks of the desired metal placed inside the wafer. As current flows through the filament, it starts to glow. The coils get so hot that the metal inside melts. As the filament gets even hotter, the metal finally starts to evaporate. The evaporated metal atoms fly around in the hot gas. They eventually hit cooler surfaces and form a layer of condensation. They condense onto everything inside the chamber, including the wafer.

■ Removing a Layer

There are chemicals that etch out unnecessary material on wafer. Pouring a certain wet chemical on the wafer causes a reaction with the deposited material, and dissolves the surface. Once dissolved, the wafer is washed. This process is called etching.

◼ Photolithography

Specific strips can be selected by coating the wafer with a light sensitive protectant known as resist, or photoresist. By using the properties of resist, the areas processed can be sorted. The blasting, gassing and condensation will only stay in the places which are not protected.

◼ Planarization

After so much digging and building to the surface of the wafer, it can become very uneven, especially after a few layers. Thus the surface needs to be etched, grinded or polished to make it flat again. Making a flat plane for the next layer is called planarization. Without this process, a new layer might undulate down, up and over some pretty stiff turns and valleys. The turning causes stress at each bend, and the material stretches thin around tight angles.

◼ Mask

The physical mask layout of any circuit to be manufactured using a particular process must conform to a set of geometric constraints or rules, which are generally called layout design rules[1].

The design rules dictate spacings between wells, sizes of contacts, minimum spacing between a poly and a metal and many other similar rules. Other rules include minimum feature dimensions and minimum allowable separations between two such features. If a metal line width

---

[1] There are two types of layout design rules, micron and lambda rules. In micron rules, the layout constraints such as minimum feature sizes and minimum allowable feature separations, are stated in terms of absolute dimensions in micrometers. On the other hand, lambda rules specify the layout constraints in terms of a single parameter (λ) and, thus, allow linear scaling of all geometrical constraints. Refer to Appendix A. MOSIS layout design rule.

is made too small, for example, it is possible that the line can break during the fabrication process or afterwards, resulting in an open circuit. If two lines are placed too close to each other in the layout, they may form an unwanted short circuit by merging during or after the fabrication process. In other words, design rules are essential to any successful layout design, since they account for the various allowances that need to be given during actual fabrication and they account for the sizes and the steps involved in generating masks for the final layout. Therefore, before drawing a layout, first it is necessary to understand the design rules for layout. The main objective of design rules is to achieve a high overall yield and reliability while using the smallest possible silicon area, for any circuit to be manufactured with a particular process.

2.4 Layout Design Examples

The initial phase of layout design can be simplified significantly by the use of stick diagrams as shown in Fig.2.8. A stick diagram is a simplified layout form, which contains information related to each of the process steps, but does not contain the actual size of the individual features.

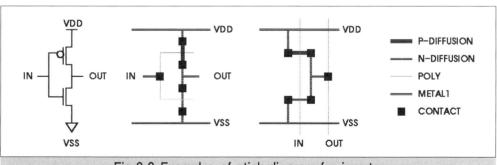

Fig.2.8 Examples of stick diagram for inverter

The purpose of the stick diagram is to provide the designer a good understanding of the topological constraints, and to quickly test several possibilities for the optimum layout without actually drawing a complete mask diagram. The stick diagram can easily be drawn by hand and is a handy intermediate form between the circuit diagram and the physical layout since it can easily be modified and corrected. It can therefore be used to anticipate and avoid possible problems when laying out the circuit.

■ CMOS INVERTER

In Fig.2.9, the mask layout design of a CMOS inverter will be examined step-by-step. Although the circuit consists of one NMOS and one PMOS transistor, there exists a number of different design possibilities even for this very simple circuit. Fig.2.8 shows two such possibilities.

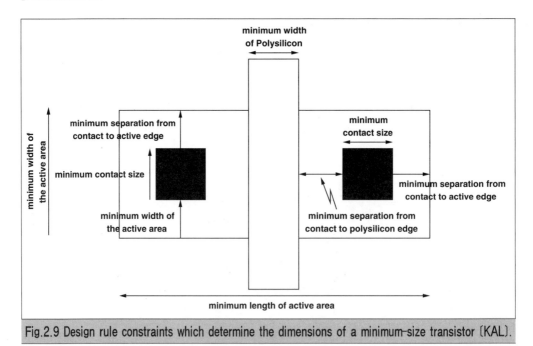

Fig.2.9 Design rule constraints which determine the dimensions of a minimum-size transistor [KAL].

First, it is necessary to create the individual transistors according to the design rules (Fig.2.9). Assume that the design goal is to design an inverter with minimum-size transistors. The width of the active area is then determined by the minimum diffusion contact size (which is necessary for source and drain connections) and the minimum separation from diffusion contact to both active area edges. The width of the polysilicon line over the active area (which is the gate of the transistor) is typically taken as the minimum poly width.

Then, the overall length of the active area is simply determined by the following sum: (minimum poly width) + 2 x (minimum poly-to - contact spacing) + 2 x (minimum spacing from contact to active area edge). The PMOS transistor must be placed in an n-well region, and the minimum size of the n-well is dictated by the PMOS active area and the minimum n-well overlap over n+. The distance between the NMOS and the PMOS transistor is determined by the minimum separation between the n+ active area and the n-well (Fig.2.10 (a)). The polysilicon gates of the NMOS and the PMOS transistors are usually aligned.

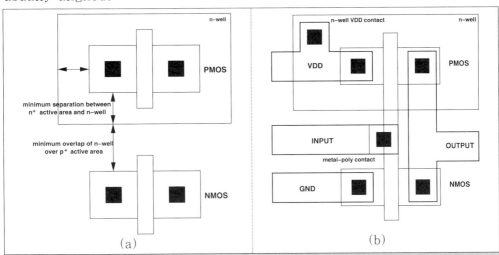

Fig.2.10 (a) Placement of one NMOS and one PMOS transistor, and (b) Complete mask layout of the CMOS inverter [KAL].

The final step in the mask layout is the local interconnections in metal, for the output node and for the VDD and GND contacts (Fig.2.10 (b)). Notice that in order to be biased properly, the n-well region must also have a VDD contact.

■ NAND2 and NOR2

Fig.2.11 shows the sample layouts of a two-input NAND gate and a two-input NOR gate, using single-layer polysilicon and single-layer metal. Here, the p-type diffusion area for the PMOS transistors and the n-type diffusion area for the NMOS transistors are aligned in parallel to allow simple routing of the gate signals with two parallel polysilicon lines running vertically. Also notice that the two mask layouts show a very strong symmetry, due to the fact that the NAND and the NOR gates have a symmetrical circuit topology.

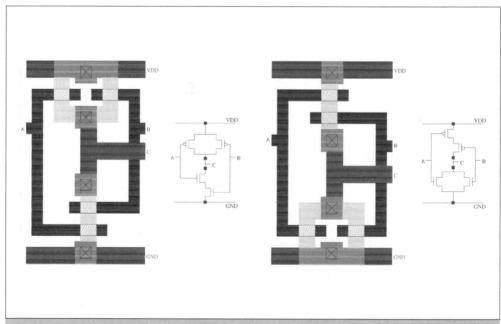

Fig.2.11 Sample layouts of a CMOS NAND2 gate and a CMOS NOR2 gate [WAE]

■ Complex CMOS Logic Gate Design

The design steps for a more complex CMOS logic, for example AOI22, are the following:

First, construct a logic graph of the schematic (Fig.2.12 (a)) using the following steps:

    a. Identify each transistor with a unique name (A, B, C, and D as in the example).

    b. Identify each connection to the transistor with a unique name (n1, n2, n3 in the example).

Next, construct one Euler path for both the Pull up and Pull down network (Fig.2.12 (b)).

    a. Euler paths are defined by a path, such that each edge is visited only once.

    b. A path is defined by the order of each transistor name. If the path traverses transistor A, B, and C, then the path name is {A, B, C}.

    c. The Euler path of the Pullup network must be the same as the path of the Pull-down network.

    d. Euler paths are not necessarily unique.

Finally, once the Euler path is found, it is time to draw the stick-diagram (See Fig.2.12(c)). The final step is to draw the layout.

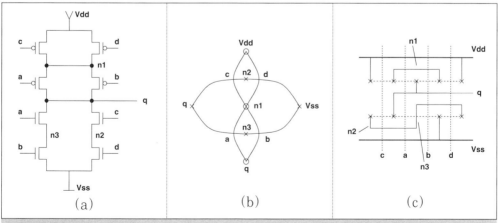

(a)   (b)   (c)

Fig.2.12 An example of (a) Schematic, (b) Euler Path, and (c) Stick Diagram.

2.5	Layout Considerations

▣ Device Sizing

Fig.2.13 shows a basic transistor which is built from a polysilicon gate, placed over a region of thin silicon dioxide. In the figure, the rectangle represents the edges of the gate material and the other rectangle depicts the edges of the thin oxide area. The oxide layer is referred to as the active layer. The active is where atoms will be implanted to create a transistor. The overlap of the gate and active layers determine the size of the device.

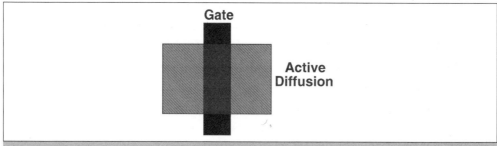

Fig.2.13 Top layout view of an MOS transistor showing gate area and active diffusion area.

Before deciding the size, a designer needs to know at which frequency the circuit must operate. For example, a circuit designer might be given a list of requirements that says "The target multiplier must be running at 50 MHz and take 0.1 mA from a 3.3 V supply." This is the starting point where the numbers are called the circuit specifications, or specs. With detailed information about a particular process, the specs can determine the necessary device sizes. Many different circuit techniques can be used to design a component such as a multiplier. A designer chooses a circuit topology among them that will give the required performance. Then, the designer calculates the basic capabilities of the circuit and verifies that the circuit meets the specs.

The way to verify IC design assumptions is to build the circuit and run it. The designer runs the design through a computer program called a simulator. The simulation program indicates what the circuit does, how much current it consumes, the frequency response, etc. These circuit simulation programs are commonly called Simulation Program for Integrated Circuits Emphasis (SPICE). The original SPICE was developed by the University of California at Berkeley in the 1970's. Running a simulation is cheaper and faster than building a chip.

In order for SPICE to accurately predict the complex behaviors of a circuit, a mathematical representation of the circuit elements is needed. This is called a model. The model accurately reflects the physics of the device and its electrical and physical characters. The SPICE simulation results show how the circuit performs with the given device sizes and values. Since the input values in the simulation deck can be adjusted easily, the simulator allows designers to sweep the input data, and they can tune the device sizes and values to optimize the design. Some layout tips are found in the following subsections [SNT, BTT, CLN].

■ Long and Thin Transistors

Many processes have a design rule specifying the maximum width of a transistor to ensure effective current conduction at the end opposite the driving signal. When larger transistors are required (e.g. in buffers to drive cross-chip or off-chip signals), many smaller transistors can be connected in parallel to achieve the same effect.

CMOS VLSI Layout Artwork Design and Lab ·······································

In reality, the resistance and capacitance are evenly distributed along the width of the gate. The gate voltage will rise and fall according to the RC time constant. These parasitic elements prevent the device from operating optimally. Since the transistor gate width defines the speed at which the transistor switches, the gate width cannot be changed. Thus, the effective gate width should be maintained.

A long transistor can be split into several smaller transistors that are hooked up in parallel. This is the same size transistor with the same effective gate width, but with less parasitic resistance. In Fig.2.14, each individual transistor has a Gate finger that is one fourth of the width of the original device. This means that the gate finger has a resistance that is one fourth of the resistance of the original device. In addition, the gate fingers are wired in parallel. Four equal resistors in parallel yield an overall resistance of one fourth of the individual resistance value. The overall effect of this splitting technique gives a parasitic resistance that is one sixteenth of the original.

Next, leg transistors can optimize routing and achieve diffusion sharing. Legging refers to the process of splitting a very wide transistor into a number of narrower parallel transistors with the equivalent overall drive strength. For example if a 32 μm transistor is split into four parallel 8 μm transistors, the entire structure is referred to as a four-leg transistor. Fig.2.14 shows an example of a four-legged transistor. Besides being necessary for wide transistors, legging can also aid routing and layout density. By choosing to leg a transistor, its aspect ratio may be better suited to the available space. Also, with the choice of an even or odd number of legs and which nodes are source and drain, additional opportunities for diffusion sharing may be exposed. For example, imagine a transistor connecting to VDD and some signal out. If no other transistor has a diffusion connection to out, then this transistor may only share diffusion on the VDD side. However, if the transistor were legged by a factor of two with out in the center and VDD on either side, any transistor connecting to VDD could share with either side of the legged transistor.

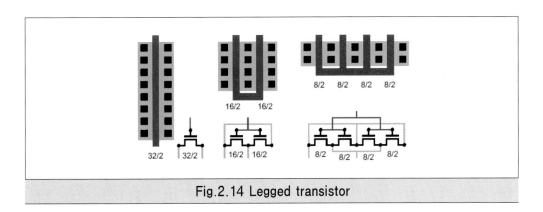

Fig.2.14 Legged transistor

■ Routing Layer usage

One of the earliest and most important decisions is the metal layer usage. There are a finite number of layers available for routing, and they have unique characteristics. Polysilicon has a high resistance, but it can be useful for short interconnections, especially if it turns into a gate at some point. Metal-1 (M1) is moderately narrow, fairly low in resistance, and easily accessible, making it ideal for local interconnect. Metal-2 (M2) often has a lower resistance, usually because it is thicker or wider, but has larger space requirements and is harder to access. An M2 connection to a transistor gate, for example, requires a sizable space for a contact, a via, and the required poly, M1, and M2 landing pads (the wider metal areas surrounding vias). Therefore, in a two metal process, M2 is used for global routing. Higher metal layers are often reserved for long distance routing and global signals that require low resistance paths such as clocks and power.

Fig.2.15 shows the wiring completed. All the A terminals have been connected in metal deposited in strips above the device. Note that the fingers of metal reaching down each terminal are all connected together at the top of the diagram. The same technique can be used to join the two B terminals. Metal fingers reach up into each B terminal, joining together at the bottom of the diagram. The gate connections are slightly different in that polysilicon is used. Using polysilicon as a wire is only recommended for very short distances because polysilicon is much more resistive than metal.

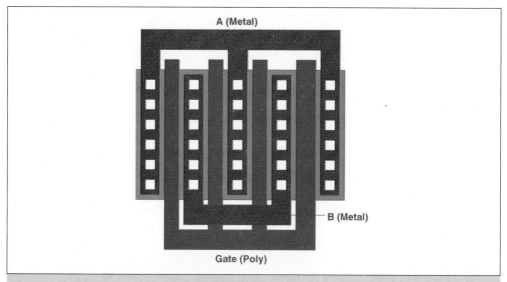

Fig.2.15 All sources, drains and Gates connected. This has the same effective Gate width as one long and thin transistor.

Another tip is to never terminate a long route (greater than ~ 100μm) with a diffusion region (transistor source-drain; e.g. a pass gate). Electromagnetic (transmission line) effects can cause signals to exceed VDD or drop below GND momentarily, potentially forward biasing the source/drain-substrate/well diode. Long distance signals should always end at the gate of a transistor instead. This can be accomplished by placing one or two inverters between the long wire and the pass gate (usually a MUX). Obviously, if only one inverter is inserted, the logic before or after the gate will have to be adjusted.

Note that it is needed to minimize the number of times a signal switches between routing layers. Contacts and vias have resistance that can be equal to fairly long metal lines. For this reason, poly may be a better choice than M1 for very short routes between gates.

It is necessary to avoid driving one transistor through another. In other words, do not chain transistors together via their gates as shown in Fig.2.16. The combination of high poly sheet resistance and gate capacitance can cause such signals to switch very slowly. However, it is common to use the same poly line to drive complementary transistors (such as in an inverter). In this case, connect the driving signal to the poly (that forms the two gates) between the two transistors. Obviously, the impact of driving one transistor through another is more pronounced with wider transistors. Therefore, if routing is significantly simplified by going against this recommendation in a specific case, consideration should be given to the widths of the transistors involved.

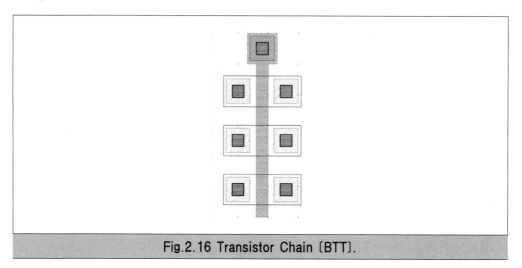

Fig.2.16 Transistor Chain (BTT).

▣ Compact Layout

Most ICs are designed using very small circuits, which are easier to handle, and to understand the designs. These little circuits are then wired together to create a larger, more complex circuit. This approach to circuit design makes layout much easier. Instead of trying to determine how to wire twelve million transistors in one go, it is better to start with a circuit that has twelve and creep up on the larger problem. The goal is to compact layouts. A rectangular circuit layout is much easier to use in conjunction with one million other rectangular circuit blocks than irregularly shaped lumpy circuit layouts.

Next, sharing diffusion regions of interconnected transistors minimizes both area and load capacitance, which it thus improves switching speed. There are a number of techniques that optimize diffusion sharing. If the particular junction being shared is connected to VDD or GND, it is acceptable to widen the diffusion region (increase the intra-gate distance) to allow one additional metal line to cross the diffusion beside the connection to the supply as shown in

Fig.2.17. The extra diffusion capacitance is acceptable since the supply node is always at the same potential Since one of the transistors will see an increased resistance to the supply rail, however, the widening should be limited to accommodate a single extra line.

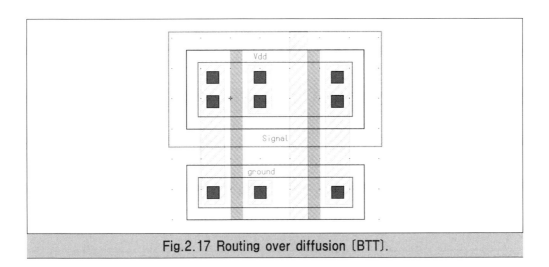

Fig.2.17 Routing over diffusion (BTT).

One of the largest design rules in many processes is the well separation distance. In addition, each well needs at least one well tap to ensure that the well is at the proper electrical potential. To minimize the area consumption by meeting these requirements, wells in subcells are often extended to the cell boundary if an adjacent cell contains a similarly placed well (sharing wells across cell boundaries). Well taps are then added at the top level for the shared well. All real-world processes have a design rule for the area of the well or substrate that can be covered by a given tap. As the distance to the tap increases, the substrate/well resistance causes the bulk voltage to deviate farther from the ideal value. In an extreme case, the result can be the forward biasing of the diode that exists between the source and the substrate/well resulting in latch-up or other undesired effects.

It is necessary to strap transistor source and drain junctions with as many contacts as possible. Place one contact as close as design rules allow to each end of the source and drain and spread as many additional contacts as possible between the ones on either end (Fig.2.17 (a)). This ensures that the entire width of the device is useful in drain current conduction.

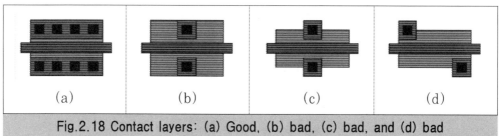

(a)   (b)   (c)   (d)

Fig.2.18 Contact layers: (a) Good, (b) bad, (c) bad, and (d) bad

References

[SNT] C. Saint and J. Saint, *IC Layout Basics: A Practical Guide*, McGraw-Hill, 2001.

[KAL] S.M. Kang and Y. Leblebici, CMOS *Digital Integrated Circuits: Analysis and Design*, McGraw-Hill, Second Edition, 1999.

[WAE] N.H.E. Weste and K. Eshraghian, *Principles of CMOS VLSI Design*, Addison-Wesley Publishing Company, Second Edition, 1993.

[RAB] J.M. Rabaey, *Digital Integrated Circuits*, Prentice Hall, 1996.

[MJS] Michael John Sebastian and John Smith, *Application-Specific Integrated Circuits*, Wesley Publishing Company, 1997.

[CLN] Dan Clein, *CMOS IC Layout*, Newnes Publications. 2000.

[BTT] J.A. Butts (2001, December), Layout Tips and Techniques. Available:
http://www.cs.wisc.edu/~butts/layout.html.

LAB1. Analysis of RC in CMOS

RC Modeling & Spice Simulation

In this lab, we will draw a CMOS layout using MyCAD. And after parameter (netlist) extraction from the layout, you will simulate the netlist using a SPICE simulator. The goal of this lab is to optimize CMOS layout (minimize area) and study the causes and results of rising and falling delays in CMOS.

In this lab, we will study an RC model to evaluate the propagation delays of a CMOS circuit. This model requires us to estimate two parameters, R and C. If we can ignore the wiring effects (the resistance and capacitance of interconnecting wires), the R is the overall effective channel resistance of the pull-up (or pull-down) network and the C is the total capacitance at the output node. The output node C consists of two capacitors. One capacitor is due to the diffusion areas (i.e., drain areas) of the driver and the other comes from the input capacitance (i.e., gate capacitance) of the receivers as shown in the following figure.

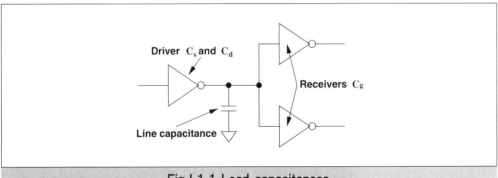

Fig.L1.1 Load capacitances.

For a given fabrication process, test circuits can be created and measured to determine the parameters for propagation delay estimation:

Rsn – Effective channel sheet resistance for nMOS transistors

Rsp – Effective channel sheet resistance for pMOS transistors

$$R = \frac{\rho}{t} \frac{l}{w} [\Omega]$$

where, ρ : resistivity, t : thickness, l/w : length of TR / width of TR

Alternatively as

$$R = R_s \frac{l}{w}$$

where, R_s : sheet resistance in [Ω/square]

Cg – Gate capacitance per unit area

Cd – Drain capacitance per unit area. In practice, drain capacitance consists of bottom-wall and side-wall capacitances. We are simplifying it by considering bottom-wall capacitance only.

▣ Procedure Overview

Step 1: Drawing an Inverter using MyChip

   1. Create the layout of an inverter(L = 6λ, W = 12λ)

   2. Extract inverter's netlist.

Step 2: Make a chain of three identical inverters and use SPICE to find the delay time of the 3rd inverter (from input to output of the inverter) in the spice netlist.

1. Make a spice input file - lab1.cir
2. Set up the following equations:
   Tplh = Rsp * (L/W) * Cd * (drain areas)
   Tphl = Rsn * (L/W) * Cd * (drain areas)

Step 3: The following spice frame includes a large capacitor (0.1pF) to the output of the inverter that you use in Step 1. Insert your spice netlist into this frame and find the 3rd inverter's delay time of this circuit.

1. Make another spice netlist input file - lab1_cap.cir
2. Set up the following equations:
   Tplh = Rsp * (L/W) * (Cd * (drain areas) + 0.1pF)
   Tphl = Rsn * (L/W) * (Cd * (drain areas) + 0.1pF)

Step 4: In the next spice frame, an identical inverter is connected to the output of the inverter that you use in Step 1. Find the delay time of the 3rd inverter.

1. Make another spice netlist input file - lab1_inv.cir
2. Set up the following equations:
   Tplh = Rsp * (L/W) * (Cd * (drain areas) + Cg * (2*L*W))
   Tphl = Rsn * (L/W) * (Cd * (drain areas) + Cg * (2*L*W))

Step 5: Solve all the equations to find Cg, Cd, Rsp and Rsn.

STEP 1 | **Pre-Lab**

Follow the pre-lab for creating a CMOS inverter (See P.11~P.19).

STEP 2~4 | **Running MySPICE and RC Modeling**

The next step is to prepare a Spice circuit file that includes the created netlist, and specifies inputs and DC supply voltages, types of analyses to be performed, analysis options, and device models. This file can be prepared using a PC text editor. Here is the example file:

```
CMOS inverter test
*

* define global parameter
.GLOBAL GND:G VDD:P
*

* include model parameters:
.include c:\MyCAD\mosis2u.spi
*

* supply voltages:
Vgnd GND 0 dc 0
VDD VDD 0 dc 5
*

* input voltage source:
Vin input 0 dc 2.92 pulse(0 5 1n 0.1n 0.1n 2n 4n)
*

* analyses and options:
.dc vin 0 5 0.005
.tran 0.01n 4n
.tf v(out) Vin
.ac dec 10 100 1000meg
*

* options:
.options abstol=1uA vntol=1mV reltol=0.01
*

* define sub-circuit
.SUBCKT inverter IN OUT
M1 OUT IN GND GND NMOS W=2.6U L=1U AS=7.28P PS=8.2U
AD=7.28P
```

+ PD=8.2U

M2 OUT IN VDD VDD PMOS W=2.6U L=1U AS=7.54P PS=8.4U AD=7.28P

+ PD=8.2U

.ends

*

* define instances

Xinv1 input tmp1 inverter

Xinv2 tmp1 IN inverter

Xinv3 IN OUT inverter

*

*define passive elements

Ccap1 OUT GND 0.1pF

*.end

The first line in the file is reserved for the title. The lines starting with * are comments. The **.include** line includes the contents of the specified file. Here is the mosis2u.spi (with the appropriate path) that contains the device parameters for the target technology. Next several lines specify the supply voltages and the input voltage. **.options** command line specifies the desired accuracy of simulation results in .tran analyses. The parameters included here usually give results with good numerical accuracy and without convergence problems that sometimes prevent completion of numerical algorithms used in the simulator:

abstol = **x**: Resets the absolute current error tolerance of the program.

The default value is 1 picoamp.

vntol = **x**: Resets the absolute voltage error tolerance of the program.

The default value is 1 microvolt.

reltol = **x**: Resets the relative error tolerance of the program.

The default value is 0.001 (0.1 %).

Let's discuss the usage of .SUBCKT, m~, C~, and X~ and others more detail in the above example.

.SUBCKT subnam N1 ⟨N2 N3 ...⟩

Example:

.SUBCKT OPAMP 1 2 3 4

A circuit definition is begun with a .SUBCKT line. SUBNAM is the subcircuit name, and N1, N2, ... are the external nodes, which cannot be zero. The group of element lines which immediately follow the .SUBCKT line define the subcircuit. The last line in a subcircuit definition is the .ENDS line. Control lines may not appear within a subcircuit definition; however, subcircuit definitions may contain anything else, including other subcircuit definitions, device models, and subcircuit calls. Note that any device models or subcircuit definitions included as part of a subcircuit definition are strictly local (i.e., such models and definitions are not known outside the subcircuit definition). Also, any element nodes not included on the .SUBCKT line are strictly local, with the exception of 0 (ground) which is always global.

M~ ND NG NS NB MNAME ⟨L=VAL⟩ ⟨W=VAL⟩ ⟨AD=VAL⟩ ⟨AS=VAL⟩
+ ⟨PD=VAL⟩ ⟨PS=VAL⟩ ⟨NRD=VAL⟩ ⟨NRS=VAL⟩ ⟨OFF⟩
+ ⟨IC=VDS, VGS, VBS⟩ ⟨TEMP=T⟩

Example:

M124 2 0 20TYPE1

M31 2 17 6 10 MODM L=5U W=2U

M1 2 9 3 0MOD1 L=10U W=5U AD=100P AS=100P PD=40U PS=40U

ND, NG, NS, and NB are the drain, gate, source, and bulk (substrate) nodes, respectively. MNAME is the model name. L and W are the channel length and width, in meters. AD and AS are the areas of the drain and source diffusions, in meters^2. Note that the suffix U specifies microns (1e-6 m) and P sq-microns (1e-12 m^2). If any of L, W, AD, or AS are not specified, default values are used. The use of defaults simplifies input file preparation, as well as the editing required if device geometries are to be changed. PD and PS are the perimeters of the drain and source junctions, in meters. NRD and NRS designate the equivalent number of squares of the drain and source diffusions; these values multiply the sheet resistance RSH specified on the .MODEL control line for an accurate representation of the parasitic series drain and source resistance of each transistor. PD and PS default to 0.0 while NRD and NRS to 1.0. OFF indicates an (optional) initial condition on the device for dc analysis. The (optional) initial condition specification using IC=VDS, VGS, VBS is intended for use with the UIC option on the .TRAN control line, when a transient analysis is desired starting from other than the quiescent operating point. See the .IC control line for a better and more convenient way to specify transient initial conditions. The (optional) TEMP value is the temperature at which this device is to operate, and overrides the temperature specification on the .OPTION control line. The temperature specification is ONLY valid for level 1, 2, 3, and 6 MOSFETs, not for level 4 or 5 (BSIM) devices.

C~ N+ N⁻ VALUE ⟨IC=INCOND⟩

Example:

CBYP 13 0 1UF
COSC 17 23 10U IC=3V

N+ and N⁻ are the positive and negative element nodes, respectively. VALUE is the capacitance in Farads. The (optional) initial condition is the initial (time-zero) value of capacitor voltage (in Volts). Note that the initial conditions (if any) apply ′ only′ if the UIC option is specified on the .TRAN control line.

X~ N1 〈N2 N3 ...〉 SUBNAM

Example:

X1 2 4 17 3 1MULTI

Subcircuits are used in SPICE by specifying pseudo-elements beginning with the letter X, followed by the circuit nodes to be used in expanding the subcircuit.

.INCLUDE *filename*

Example:

.INCLUDE /users/spice/common/wattmeter.cir

Frequently, portions of circuit descriptions will be reused in several input files, particularly with common models and subcircuits. In any spice input file, the ″.include″ line may be used to copy some other file as if that second file appeared in place of the ″.include″ line in the original file. There is no restriction on the file name imposed by spice beyond those imposed by the local operating system.

PULSE(V1 V2 TD TR TF PW PER)

Example:

VIN 3 0 PULSE(-1 1 2NS 2NS 2NS 50NS 100NS)

parameter	default value	units
V1 (initial value)	–	Volts or Amps
V2 (pulsed value)	–	Volts or Amps
TD (delay time)	0.0	seconds
TR (rise time)	TSTEP	seconds
TF (fall time)	TSTEP	seconds
PW (pulse width)	TSTOP	seconds
PER(period)	TSTOP	seconds

A single pulse so specified is described by the following table:

time	value
0	V1
TD	V1
TD + TR	V2
TD + TR + PW	V2
TD + TR + PW + TF	V1
TSTOP	V1

.TRAN TSTEP TSTOP ⟨TSTART ⟨TMAX⟩⟩

Example:

.TRAN 1NS 100NS
.TRAN 1NS 1000NS 500NS
.TRAN 10NS 1US

TSTEP is the printing or plotting increment for line-printer output. For use with the post-processor, TSTEP is the suggested computing increment. TSTOP is the final time, and TSTART is the initial time. If TSTART is omitted, it is assumed to be zero. The transient analysis always begins at time zero. In the interval ⟨zero, TSTART⟩, the circuit is analyzed (to reach a steady state), but no outputs are stored. In the interval ⟨TSTART, TSTOP⟩, the circuit is analyzed and outputs are stored. TMAX is the maximum step-size that SPICE uses; for default, the program chooses either TSTEP or (TSTOP-TSTART)/50.0, whichever is smaller. TMAX is useful when one wishes to guarantee a computing interval which is smaller than the printer increment, TSTEP. UIC (use initial conditions) is an optional keyword which indicates that the user does not want SPICE to solve for the quiescent operating point before beginning the transient analysis. If this keyword is specified, SPICE uses the values specified using IC=... on the various elements as the initial transient condition and proceeds with the analysis. If the .IC control line has been specified, then the node voltages on the .IC line are used to compute the initial conditions for the devices. Look at the description on the .IC control line for its interpretation when UIC is not specified.

RC Modeling

R_{sn} , R_{sp} , C_g , and C_d calculations

Switching speed of MOS systems strongly dependent:

a. Resistance of transistors and wires.
b. Interconnect capacitance of wires and parasitic capacitances

associated with the MOS transistor:
  Gate capacitance (of receiver logic gates),
  Driver diffusion (source/drain) capacitance, and
  Routing (line) capacitance of substrate and other wires.

Let's consider approximations of each of these capacitances and subsequent approximations of delay based on the following expressions. Ignore the wiring effects (the resistance and capacitance of interconnecting wires) and consider bottom-wall capacitance only.

➡ The R is the overall effective channel resistance of the pull-up (or pull-down) network and the C is the total capacitance at the output node.

➡ The output node capacitance consists of two capacitors. One capacitor is due to the diffusion areas (i.e., the transistor drains) of the driving stage and the other comes from the input capacitance (i.e., the transistor gate capacitance) of the next stage (i.e., loading stage). Note that we must consider both of PMOS and NMOS areas when calculating the drain and the gate areas.

R_{sn} – *Effective channel sheet resistance for nMOS transistors*
R_{sp} – *Effective channel sheet resistance for pMOS transistors*
C_g – *Gate capacitance per unit area*
C_d – *Drain capacitance per unit area.*

Eq. 1. -- $T_{plh} = R_{sp} * (2/4) * C_d *$ (drain areas),
Eq. 2. -- $T_{phl} = R_{sn} * (2/4) * C_d *$ (drain areas),
Eq. 3. -- $T_{plh} = R_{sp} * (2/4) * (C_d *$ (drain areas) + additional

load cap),

Eq. 4. -- T_{phl} = R_{sn} * (2/4) * (C_d * (drain areas) + additional load cap),

Eq. 5. -- T_{plh} = R_{sp} * (2/4) * (C_d * (drain areas) + C_g * (gate areas)),

Eq. 6. -- T_{phl} = R_{sn} * (2/4) * (C_d * (drain areas) + C_g * (gate areas),

where drain areas (PMOS & NMOS) = W_{PD} * L_{PD} + W_{ND} * L_{ND}, and gate areas

(PMOS & NMOS) = W_{PG} * L_{PG} + W_{NG} * L_{NG}

From Eq. 1 ~ 6,

R_{sp} = _____ [$\Omega/\square$],

C_d = _____ [F/ m^2],

R_{sn} = _____ [$\Omega/\square$], and

C_g = _____ [F/ m^2]

Note that the errors come from ignoring the resistance and capacitance of interconnecting wires and considering bottom-wall capacitance only.

Questions

1. Why are 2 inverters (Xinv1 and Xinv2) needed before the CUT (Circuit Under Test - Xinv3) in the given example?
2. Why is the falling delay time faster than the rising delay time of your inverter?
3. How can you balance the inverter's rising and falling times?
4. How can you get a faster inverter?
5. How does the load capacitance (e.g., additional capacitance in the step 3) affect the delay time?

Chapter III. Logic Schematic Fundamentals

3.1	Symbol

On an integrated circuit, a MOS transistor is a 4-terminal device, as indicated by the symbol in Fig.3.1(a). An n-channel (NMOS) device is built on a p-type substrate (B terminal). The substrate is called bulk. The bulk connections for MOSFET transistors are normally connected to a power supply rail. P-channel bulk connections are typically tied to the VDD rail, and n-channel bulk connections are typically tied to the VSS rail. The n-type source (S) and drain (D) regions are the device ′output′ terminals. Gate (G) is isolated from the substrate by a thin layer of oxide. A p-channel (PMOS) device is built on an n-type substrate, with p-type source and drain regions. Depending on the voltage applied between the gate (G) and source (S) terminals, a conducting channel can be established between the drain (D) and the source (S). If the source (S) and the substrate (B) terminals are shorted together (V_{SB} = 0.0 V), the MOS transistor can be considered a 3-terminal device, and the symbols in Fig.3.1(b) and (c) are in use.

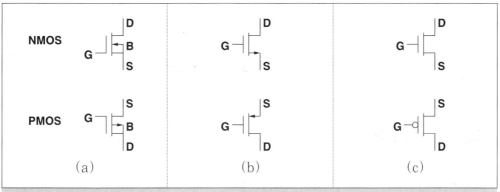

Fig.3.1 Schematic Symbols for the MOSFET Transistor [MJS]

In Fig.3.1(c), the bulk-substrate connection is not indicated and the PMOS is identified by a bubble on the gate input. The NMOS does not have a bubble. The presence of a bubble on the PMOS indicates that this device should have a logic low applied to the gate input to turn-on the transistor. The absence of a bubble on the NMOS indicates that this device should have a logic high applied to the input to turn-on the device.

Logic symbols represent a block of circuitry which perform a specific function. There are various logic gates such as AND, OR, XOR, Flip-Flop, and Buffer, all of which can be customized to handle any number of inputs and negate any signal. Negation is accomplished by placing an inverting bubble on the connecting wire rather than on the component. The Flip-Flop can be parameterized in its triggering (master-slave, positive, or negative) and in its function (RS type, JK type, or D type). Fig.3.2 shows some typical logic symbols.

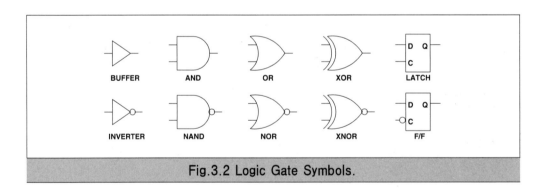

Fig.3.2 Logic Gate Symbols.

3.2 Schematic

A schematic is a drawing of an electrical circuit which shows all of the components and the electrical connections between them. A well-drawn schematic makes the function of a circuit easier to understand and aids in troubleshooting. A poor schematic on the other hand only creates confusion. All components are given unique names (references) which are used to identify them. Usually, all the component types and values and other important component specific information is shown.

In implementing the layout of any schematic, connections appear on a schematic as a simple line drawn from one point to another point, or a simple connection of two transistors in series or in parallel. In reality, a line represents a signal path that needs to be physically implemented and optimized. Fig.3.3 shows some pictorial definitions of objects in a simple schematic. Each of the cells on a schematic has a cell name. Each use of a cell is a different instance of that cell, and each instance is given a unique instance name. Each cell instance is represented by a symbol such as NAND or NOR gate. A circuit designer may also wish to attach an attribute, or property, which describes some aspect of the component, cell instance, net, or connector.

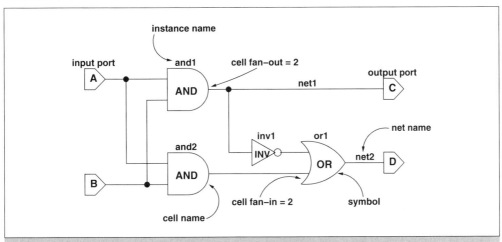

Fig.3.3 Terms used in circuit schematics.

Symbols are useful when creating designs where it is impractical to show every transistor on the top level schematic (hierarchical designs). Instead, symbols of the cells are created in order to instantiate them in the higher level schematics and make them more readable. The hierarchy approach is very similar to the software design where large programs are split into smaller and smaller sections (subroutines), with well-defined functions and interfaces. When using hierarchy to manage design complexity, the designer needs to perform an additional step. The user must create a schematic symbol for the reusable design. This symbol contains pins that interface the top-level design with the nets and gates in the design macro.

Fig.3.4 demonstrates the idea of hierarchy – a two-input multiplexor is placed in a new schematic symbol shown at the top-level schematic design (Fig.3.4(b)). At the top-level, a new schematic symbol represents the two-input multiplexor (MUX). These schematic symbols can be reused in more than one schematic. Each primitive cell instance in this schematic contains a unique name, for example, 'or1' and 'or2'.

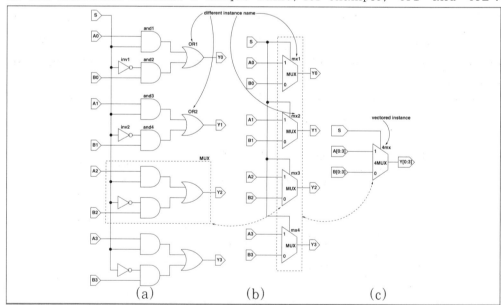

Fig.3.4 A two input 4-bit MUX: (a) drawn as a flat schematic from gate-level primitives, (b) drawn as four instances of the cell symbol MUX, and (c) drawn using a vectored instance of the MUX cell symbol.

3.3	CMOS Logic Family

3.3.1 *Combinational CMOS Logic*

Logic gates are implemented directly or in combination to form Boolean logic functions. Theoretically, almost any Boolean logic function can be implemented with a single logic gate, but in practice this is not done. Generally, most logic functions are implemented in CMOS using inverters, two to four input NANDs, two to four input NORs, and transmission gates. Note that a logic gate could be confused with the gate of a transistor.

■ NAND and NOR Gates

Both the two-input NAND gate and the two-input NOR gate consist of 4-transistors as shown in Fig.3.5. The n-channel and p-channel transistor switches implement the ′1′s and ′0′s of the output. By following the operation of the individual transistors under each input condition, Fig.3.5(a) illustrates that the desired output of 2 input NAND gate is produced with the transistor configuration shown. The NAND function (F = 0) is produced when both inputs A and B are 1. The requirement for both inputs to be 1 simultaneously is achieved by connecting the two NMOS transistors in series. At the same time, the PMOS transistors are connected in a complementary fashion by being in parallel. This configuration not only produces the correct functionality for the gate, but also results in eliminating static DC power consumption by ensuring that there is never a condition in which a PMOS path to VDD and an NMOS path to VSS are ON simultaneously.

The NOR gate is the mirror or complementary configuration of the

NAND. In the NOR gate the series/parallel connections are reversed between the NMOS and PMOS transistors as shown in Fig.3.5(b). Three or more input NAND/NOR gates are easily implemented by extending the series connections of the NMOS/PMOS transistors and the parallel connections of the PMOS/NMOS transistors.

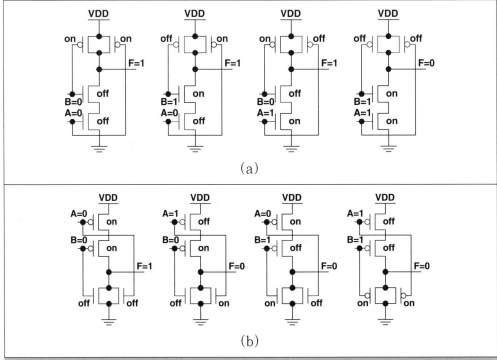

Fig.3.5 CMOS logic. (a) A two-input NAND logic cell. (b) A two-input NOR logic cell [MJS].

■ AND-OR-INVERT (AOI) and OR-AND-INVERT (OAI) Gates

As mentioned previously, almost any Boolean logic function can be implemented in a single-stage CMOS logic gate. The term complex gates is the name given to logic gates that have a complex function, usually a combination of AND, OR, NAND, and NOR. Because complex gates are implemented in a single-state, in almost all cases power consumption, area and speed benefits are achieved. The AOI and the OAI logic cells are particularly efficient in CMOS. Conceptually, an AOI logic block is a three-level logic circuit consisting of AND gates at the first level, an OR gate at the second level, and an inverter at the output. Similarly, an OAI block has OR gates at the first level, an AND gate at the second level, and an inverter at the third level.

Fig.3.6 is an example of a complex logic function implemented in multiple gates. The particular circuit in Fig.3.6(a) is called a two-input two-stack AOI gate. This means it consists of two 2-input AND gates (each AND gate corresponds to a stack). A three-input two-stack AOI gate has two 3-input gates at the first level, a two-input three-stack AOI gate has three 2-input gates at the first level, and so on. The number of stacks is exactly the number of inputs to the second-level OR gate. Analogous concepts and terminology apply to OAI blocks. Fig.3.6(b) gives a possible implementation in terms of switches. If A and B are true or C and D are true, the normally open switches establish a closed path from false to output Z.

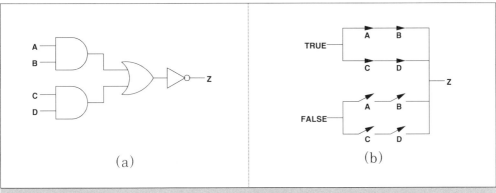

(a)   (b)

Fig.3.6 (a) An example of AOI22 logic and (b) its switch diagram

In all other cases, true will be routed to the output through the normally closed switches. For example, if A = 0, B = 1, C = 1, and D = 0, the normally closed switches controlled by A and D will be closed, making the connection between true and the output Z. Switch implementations of OAI circuits look very similar. The implementation in Fig.3.6(b) uses eight switches. If the function had been implemented using straightforward logic gates, 14 switches would be needed: four for each of the three 2-input gates and two for the inverter.

The AOI and OAI logic cells can be built using a single stage in CMOS using series-parallel networks of transistors called stacks. This type of complex gate is very efficient to use and build, but some how cumbersome to draw. To determine the transistor representation, designers analyze the logic starting from the output gate and work backward.

Fig.3.7 illustrates the procedure to build the n-channel and p-channel stacks, using the AOI22 cell as an example. Here are the steps to construct any single-stage combinational CMOS logic cell:

ⓐ Draw a schematic icon with an inversion (bubble) on the last cell (the bubble-out schematic). Use De Morgan's theorems- "A NAND is an OR with inverted inputs and a NOR is an AND with inverted inputs"-to push the output bubble back to the inputs.

ⓑ Form the n-channel stack working from the inputs on the bubble-out schematic: OR translates to a parallel connection, AND translates to a series connection. And form the p-channel stack using the bubble-in schematic.

ⓒ The two stacks can be derived from each other by swapping series connections for parallel, and parallel for series connections. The n-channel stack implements the strong '0's of the function and the p-channel stack provides the strong '1's.

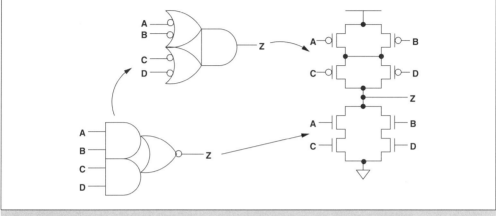

Fig.3.7 Constructing a CMOS logic cell-an AOI22 [MJS].

■ Transmission Gate (TG)

In the case of the inverter, the source of both transistors is connected to a power supply. In the case of combination gates, series connected transistors form part of a chain that eventually connects to a power supply and thus the transistors should be treated similarly to the simple inverter. However, the transmission gate is a fairly common case where both the drain and source nodes are used as signals. In this case, the output generally follows the input based on the state of the controls, S and S' in Fig.3.8(b). Note that this configuration allows for non-inverting propagation of the input signal, as well as the blocking of the input signal when both control signals disable the PMOS and NMOS transistors.

While both NMOS and PMOS transistors indeed have a very large resistance between source and drain when switched off, resistance between source and drain depends on the source and drain voltages when switched on. This resistance exists especially when there is a voltage drop (hence, bad voltage transfer characteristic) across a conducting N-type transistor when the source voltage is near VDD, or a voltage drop across a conducting PMOS transistor when its source voltage is near GND (Fig.3.8(a)).

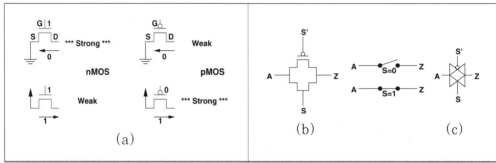

Fig.3.8 (a)The voltage characteristics of NMOS and PMOS, (b) An NMOS and PMOS in parallel form a TG. (c) And a common symbol for a TG.

Therefore, the use of single NMOS or PMOS transistors as switches is limited to circuits where the voltage drop across the conducting transistors is not critical. A series connection of transistors used as switches is usually not possible in digital circuits. But a combination of NMOS and PMOS transistors are efficient switches in CMOS technology. The circuit consists of one NMOS and one PMOS transistor connected in parallel and controlled by inverted gate voltages. This circuit is called a transmission gate. If the gate voltage of the NMOS transistor is 'GND', the PMOS transistor has a gate voltage of 'VDD' then both transistors are non-conducting. On the other hand, if the gate voltage of the NMOS transistor is 'VDD' and the gate voltage of the P-type transistor is 'GND', both transistors are conducting. If the source voltage is near VDD, there is a voltage drop across the NMOS transistor but (almost) no voltage drop across the PMOS transistor. If the source voltage is near GND, the NMOS transistor has (almost) no voltage drop.

Fig.3.8(b) and (c) shows a CMOS TG that is connected with a p-channel transistor (to transmit a strong '1') in parallel with an n-channel transistor (to transmit a strong '0'). There is a potential problem if a TG is used as a switch connecting a node Z that has a large capacitance, C_{BIG} , to an input node A that has only a small capacitance C_{SMALL} (see Fig.3.9). If the initial voltage at A is V_{SMALL} and the initial voltage at Z is V_{BIG} , and the TG (by setting S = '1') is closed, the final voltage on both nodes A and Z is

$$V_F = (C_{BIG} \, V_{BIG} + C_{SMALL} \, V_{SMALL}) \, / \, (C_{BIG} + C_{SMALL}).$$

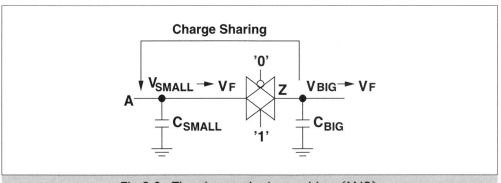

Fig.3.9 The charge-sharing problem [MJS].

For example, C_{BIG} = 0.2 pF and C_{SMALL} = 0.02 pF, V_{BIG} = 0 V and V_{SMALL} = 5 V; then

$$V_F = \{(0.2 {*} 10^{-12})(0) + (0.02 {*} 10^{-12})(5)\} / \{(0.2 {*} 10^{-12}) + (0.02 {*} 10^{-12})\} = 0.45V.$$

The big capacitor has forced node A to a voltage close to a '0'. This type of problem is known as charge sharing. Make sure that either node A is strong enough to overcome the big capacitor, or isolate node A from node Z by including a buffer between node A and node Z.

3.3.2 *Sequential Logic*

A number of different ways are shown to realize logic gates using CMOS technology. All of the logic gates described thus far have been acyclic logic gates. That is, they have no memory or clock signals; output changes in response to input changes occur almost immediately. In this subsection, the D-type Latch and Flip-Flop of digital memory circuits will be covered. These circuits are often called cyclic logic circuits. A latch consists of a single memory location with some access circuitry. And a flip-flop in an IC typically consists of two cascaded latches and perhaps some additional input logic.

■ D−Latch

A standard D-latch can be built from four 2-input NAND gates (Fig.3.10(a)). Therefore, 16 transistors are needed for one D-latch. Fig.3.10 (b) shows how a D-latch can be realized using only 10 transistors (3 inverters and 2 TGs), if both the clock and the inverted clock signal are available – a savings of 40% of transistors and therefore chip-area. In CMOS technology, TG allows efficient realizations of several important logical functions.

Note that the input TG on the left is controlled by internal clock signals, CLKN (N for negative) and CLKP (P for positive), generated from the system clock (CLK), by using two inverters (14 and 15). The feedback TG on the bottom is controlled by a pair of CLKP and CLKN. The function of the TG D-latch is very easy to understand. If the CLKP and CLKN control inputs are '1' and '0', respectively, the input TG is conducting, and the data input value is connected to the first inverter input, which generates ~D. The second inverter generates ~(~D) = D, that is, the output Q equals D. If the CLKP and CLKN control inputs are switched to '0' and '1', respectively, the first T-gate is blocked while the feedback TG is opened. Therefore, the circuit feeds its Q signal back to the first inverter (~Q) and to the second inverter ~(~Q)=Q. That is, the value of Q is stored until the CLKP input becomes '1' again.

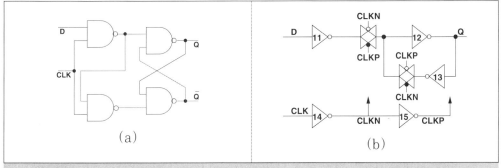

Fig.3.10 (a) 4-NAND2 Latch, and (b) Latch using TG [MRT, MJS].

A sequential logic cell is different from a combinational cell because it has this feature of storage or memory. Notice that the output Q is unbuffered and connected directly to the output of 12 (and the input of 13), which acts as a storage node. The latch of Fig.3.10(b) is a positive-enabled D latch, active-high D latch, or transparent-high D latch. A negative-enabled (active-low) D latch can be built by inverting all the clock polarities in Fig.3.10(b).

■ D–Flip–Flop

A level sensitive latch has a disadvantage in that the input signal is sampled when the latch is enabled. If only one sample of the input has to be evaluated per clock cycle, then the clock pulse width has to be made very short; this places severe timing constraints on the sequential circuit design. A simple way to solve this problem is to use a master-slave flip-flop. A master-slave (MS) flip-flop consists of a master stage and a slave stage (usually identical). These stages (D latches) however are enabled on different levels of clock signal. Fig.3.11 shows a circuit schematic of a MS D flip-flop. A digital logic device that stores the status of its "D" input whenever its clock input makes a certain transition (low to high or high to low). The output, "Q", shows the currently stored value. This flip-flop contains a total of nine inverters and four TGs. In this flip-flop design the storage node S is buffered and the clock-to-Q delay will be one inverter delay less than the clock-to-QN delay.

When the clock signal is high, the master latch is transparent and the input data D is transferred to the output of master stage M. At the same time the slave latch is disabled and it will retain its previously stored value. Therefore, the output of the D flip-flop will not change as long as CLK signal is high. As the clock goes low (the negative edge) the slave latch is enabled and will update its state and the output Q to the value of node M at the negative edge of the clock. The slave latch will then keep this value of M at the output Q, despite any changes at the D input while the clock is low. When the clock goes high again, the slave latch will store the captured value of M. Therefore, the output of the flip-flop will only store the value of the input at the falling edge of the clock and the MS flip-flop acts as a negative edge triggered circuit. This type of flip-flop is a negative-edge-triggered flip-flop and its behavior is quite different from a latch.

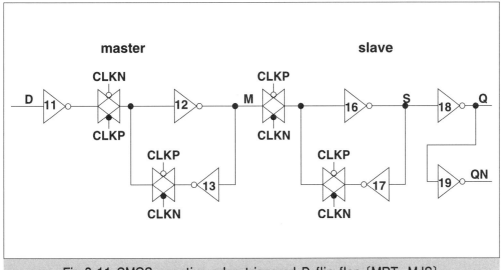

Fig.3.11 CMOS negative-edge-triggered D flip-flop (MRT, MJS).

3.4 | CMOS Inverter Voltage Transfer Characteristics

The most basic logic function and the building block for all digital circuits is the inverter. Since all other logic circuits can be reduced to an equivalent inverter, a good understanding on the static and dynamic characteristics will be useful in determining various tradeoffs between speed, area, power and noise margins of CMOS logic circuits. A CMOS inverter consists of one PMOS transistor and one NMOS transistor as shown in Fig.3.12. The PMOS transistor is connected between the power supply, VDD (source), and the output (drain). The NMOS transistor is connected between the power supply, VSS (source), and the output (drain). The gates of both transistors are connected to the input.

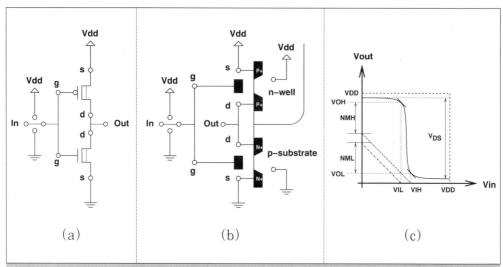

Fig.3.12 CMOS inverter's (a) schematic, (b) device cross section, and (c) voltage transfer characteristic [WAE].

Because of parasitic effects, the voltage level on internal nets may reach some undefined voltage between V_{DD} and V_{SS} after some time. A floating net will cause problems, when its voltage is around $V_{DD}/2$, because a gate voltage around $V_{DD}/2$ on either N-type or P-type transistor implies that the transistor is conducting. When both transistors are conducting, there is a direct path from V_{DD} to V_{SS}, and this implies a short-circuit condition, which dissipates much energy and may destroy the device. If the input voltage is '1' (V_{DD}) the P-type transistor on top is non-conducting, but the N-type transistor is conducting and provides a path from V_{SS} to the output. The output level therefore is '0'. On the other hand, if the input level is '0', the P-type transistor is conducting and provides a path from V_{DD} to the output, so that the output level is '1', while the N-type transistor is blocked. If the input is floating, both transistors may be conducting and a short-circuit condition is possible.

The static operation of the CMOS inverter is as follows:

ⓐ When the input voltage $V_{in} = 0$, $V_{out} = V_{OH} = V_{DD}$ and the output node is connected to V_{DD} through the resistance of the pull up transistor. Similarly, with $V_{in} = V_{DD}$, $V_{out} = V_{OL} = 0$ and the output node is connected to ground through the resistance of the pull-down transistor. Thus, in steady state, no direct-current path exists between V_{DD} and ground, and the static current and power dissipation are both zero.

ⓑ This circuit acts like the switching circuits, since the P-type transistor has exactly the opposite characteristics of the N-type transistor. Hence, when the input voltage is high, the P-type transistor is off (cutoff), and the N-type transistor is on (triode).

ⓒ When the input voltage is low, the P-type transistor is on (triode) and the N-type transistor is off (cutoff).

In the transition region, both transistors are saturated and the circuit operates with a large voltage gain. A small change in the input voltage results in a large change in the output voltage. This behavior describes an amplifier. The amplification is termed transistor gain, which is given by β. Both the n and p-channel transistors have a β. Varying their ratio will change the characteristics of the output curve. The CMOS inverter can be made to switch at the midpoint of the logic swing, 0 to V_{DD} that is at $V_{DD}/2$, by appropriately sizing the transistors. Specifically, it can be shown that the switching threshold is given by

$$V_{th} = [V_{DD} - |V_{tp}| + (k_n/k_p)^{1/2}V_{tn}]/[1 + (k_n/k_p)^{1/2}]$$

, where $k_n = k_n'(W/L)_n$ and $k_p = k_p'(W/L)_p$, from which we see that for the typical case where $V_{tn} = |V_{tp}|$, $V_{th} = V_{DD}/2$ for $k_n = k_p$, that is

$$k_n'(W/L)_n = k_p'(W/L)_p.$$

Thus, a symmetrical transfer characteristic is obtained when the devices are designed to have equal transconductance parameters, a technique referred to as matching. Since μ_n is two to three times larger than μ_p, matching is achieved by making $(W/L)_p$ two to three times $(W/L)_n$.

Normally, the two devices have the same channel length, L, which is set as the minimum allowable dimension dictated by the process technology. The minimum width of the NMOS transistor is usually one and a half to two times L, and the width of the PMOS transistor two to three times the length. If the inverter is required to drive a relatively large capacitive load, the transistors are made wider. However, to conserve chip area, most inverters would have the "minimum size".

The high noise margin (NM_H) and low noise margin (NM_L) are defined as $V_{OHmin}-V_{ILmax}$ and $V_{ILmin}-V_{OLmax}$, as shown in Fig.3.13, respectively. The maximum noise voltage on the input of a gate is defined as an unintentional input voltage variation that allows the output to remain stable. When the inverter threshold is at $V_{DD}/2$, the noise margins are equalized and their values are maximized.

Ideal characteristic: $V_{IH} = V_{IL} = (V_{OH} + V_{OL}) / 2.$

This implies that the transfer characteristic should switch abruptly (high gain in the transition region). V_{IL} is found by determining the unity gain point from V_{OH}. Qualitatively, the CMOS inverter has excellent noise margins since it has high gain in the transition region. It has low power dissipation since there is no DC current flowing in either logical state. Finally, the speed of the inverter can be set using a constant current which charges and discharges the load capacitors. These excellent characteristics have made CMOS the technology of choice for complex logic functions, as well as for semiconductor memory.

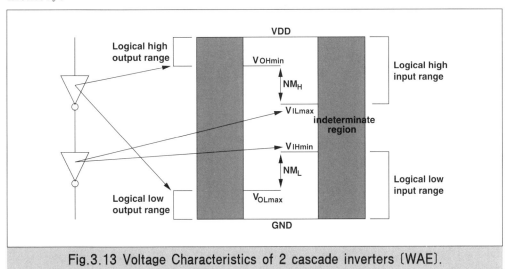

Fig.3.13 Voltage Characteristics of 2 cascade inverters [WAE].

References

[WAE] N.H.E. Weste and K. Eshraghian, *Principles of CMOS VLSI Design*, Addison-Wesley Publishing Company, Second Edition, 1993.

[MJS] Michael John Sebastian and John Smith, *Application-Specific Integrated Circuits*, Wesley Publishing Company, 1997.

[MRT] Ken Martin, *Digital Integrated Circuit Design*, Oxford University Press, Inc. 1999.

LAB2. D FLIP-FLOP Design

In this lab, you will draw the layout for a D Flip-Flop using MyChip. Upon completion of the layout and parameter extraction, you'll simulate the netlist using MySPICE. Before designing the D flip-flop, design a one-bit level-sensitive D latch. Label the input data as D, the control signal as S (store), and SB (storebar), and the output as QB. Use MyChip cell hierarchy to design the latch. In order to simplify the layout, use one inverter cell and one transmission gate as subcells in this lab. The top-level parent cell, latch, will contain four children cells, inv_0, inv_1, tg_0, and tg_1. When using cell hierarchy in MyChip, make sure that the labels, **D, QB, S**, and **SB**, are placed on a square of paint contained in the top-level parent cell, **latch**. When testing the latch, the data and control signals should not both be changing at the same time. The data should remain stable or valid as the latch control signal goes low. Then, using D latches, design a D flip-flop. Make sure that the labels of this flip-flop are D, Q, S (CLK), and SB (CLKB).

STEP 1 Design of Cells-Inverter, TG, Latch, and D F/F

The following shows the steps for designing the cells using a stick diagram:

  ❶ Design an inverter and a transmission gate whose stick diagram are as shown in Fig.L2.1. Make sure that the height of these cells is the same (<40λ), and make the cells as small as possible. You can take advantage of the inverter in Lab1 to create the transmission gate because both the transmission gate and the inverter have one PMOS and one NMOS. Modify the inverter in Lab1 to create the transmission gate. Of course, you can use the inverter itself for Lab2.

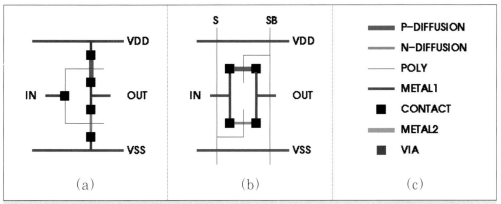

Fig.L2.1 (a) Stick diagrams of inverter and (b) transmission gate, and (c) the legend of this stick diagram

❶ Design a latch

Put two instances of an inverter and a transmission gate needed to each other on a new cell as shown in Fig.L2.2 (ignore the inverter and the transmission gate in the middle, that is an intermediate process). Merge one of the inverters and with a transmission gate in the right-upper corner of Fig.L2.2. This will now be the upper half of your CMOS latch. Flip the second inverter and transmission gate vertically and horizontally as shown below. You will now have the bottom half of your CMOS latch as shown in Fig.L2.2. **Note that you need to remove all labels when using cell hierarchy from all cells. Once the final design is completed, label this design.**

Next, merge the two halves of the latches to create a negative sensitive latch as shown in Fig.L2.3 (of course, you can layout all cells in a row instead of two rows). The polarity (QB) is not important in this latch because the flip-flop consists of two identical latches. In other words, the polarity is negative of negative, or simply positive. When merging the inverter and the transmission gates, use metal2 and via layers for routing easily (in order to avoid shorting wires) as shown by the step in Fig.L2.3. Note that the routing process only shows connectivity of cells in Fig.L2.4, thus you should compact your layout keeping minimum sizes and shortest paths.

ⓒ Design a D flip-flop

Place two instances of the latch you just created on the new cell, and merge them as shown below in Fig.L2.4. Note that the routing process only shows connectivity of cells in Fig.L2.4, thus you should compact your layout keeping minimum sizes and short paths. Don't forget to draw an N-well layer in your design.

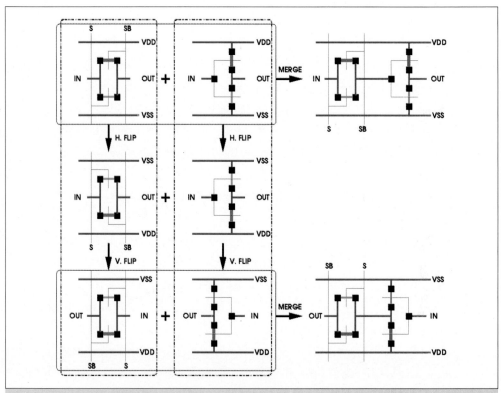

Fig.L2.2 Design steps for two different geometry half latches.

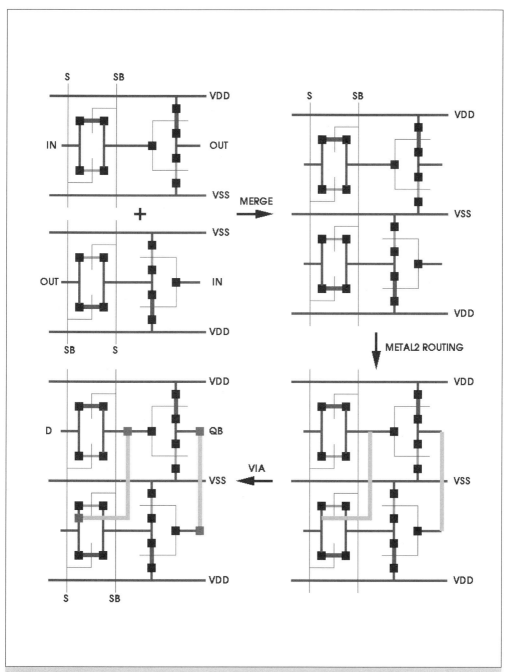

Fig.L2.3 Design steps for a negative polarity latch.

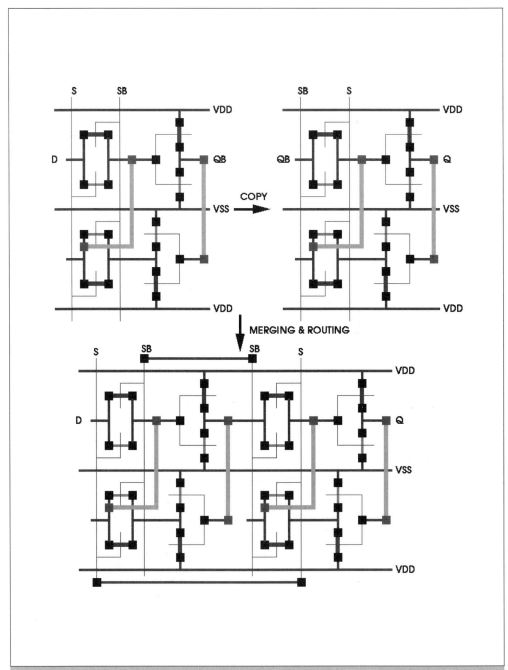

Fig.L2.4 Design steps for a D flip-flop

STEP 2 Running MySPICE

Now, we will compare the function of a latch with that of a flip-flop. The procedure of simulations is the same as that of Lab1 except for a different CUT (latch and flip-flop) and a different input file (.cir).

- ⓐ Extract Netlists: Latch and D flip-flop from MyChip.
- ⓑ Run MySPICE for latch and flip-flop.

Fig.L2.5 shows a circuit schematic of the D flip-flop in this lab. The implementation shown is based on cross-coupled latches. The first latch is clocked by S (clk), whereas the second latch is accessed on the opposite phase by SB (clkb). Thus, it is not possible for a signal to propagate from the input through both latches at one time; either the first or the second will be deactivated and in hold mode when the transmission gate in the feedback loop is active.

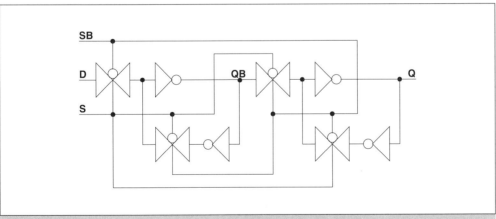

Fig.L2.5. A schematic of D flip-flop

Chapter IV. VLSI Design Styles

VLSI circuits are made on a thin (a few hundred microns thick), circular silicon wafer, with each wafer holding hundreds of die. The transistors and wiring are made from many layers (usually between 10 and 15 distinct layers) built on top of one another. Each successive mask layer has a pattern that is defined using a mask similar to a glass photographic slide. About a half-dozen layers may be used to define the transistors and the other layers define the metal wires between the transistors and the interconnect.

System designers require a rapid method of implementation on silicon to take advantage of the benefits of integration. Several design styles [WAE, SHR] such as full-custom, semi-custom, gate array and field programmable gate array can be considered for chip implementation of specified algorithms or logic functions. Each design style has its own merits and shortcomings, and thus a proper choice has to be made by designers in order to provide the functionality at low cost.

Choice of a design style depends on many factors. When volumes are large, the full custom approach with its conservation of silicon area and its optimized performance may be the answer. If time-to-market is important, it may be more appropriate to produce a standard cell design before making a commitment to the full custom approach. For modest quantities where fast turn around is essential, the gate array is appropriate. Currently manufacturers may offer a placement and routing service so that the risk involved in the gate array approach is no greater than in production of a printed circuit board. It is to be expected that all of the above approaches described will become increasingly acceptable as the Computer Aided Design (CAD) tools mature and the associated risks reduce. There is, however, a need for CAD developers to improve the rate of production of tools to keep pace with the expectations of designers as well as the rapid developments in process technology.

4.1   Full Custom Design Methodology

A full-custom IC includes possibly all logic cells and mask layers that are customized. A microprocessor is an example of a full-custom IC-designers spend many hours squeezing the most out of every last square micron of microprocessor chip space by hand. Customizing all of the IC features in this way allows designers to include analog circuits, optimized memory cells, or mechanical structures on an IC. Full-custom ICs are the most expensive to manufacture and design. The manufacturing lead-time is typically eight weeks for a full-custom IC. In digital CMOS VLSI, full-custom design is rarely used due to long design time, large investment and consequent high commercial risk. However, full custom results in the best utilization of the silicon and lowest cost for high volume production. It is useful in developing memory chips, high-performance microprocessors and FPGA masters.

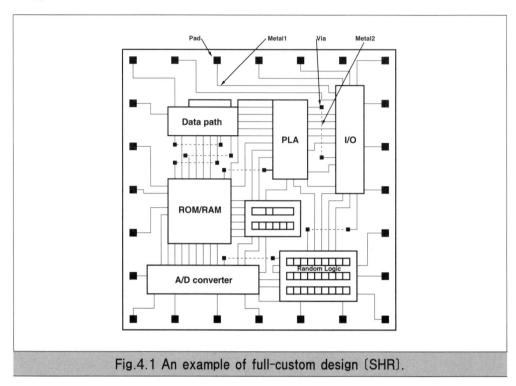

Fig.4.1 An example of full-custom design (SHR).

Fig.4.1 shows an example of a hybrid full-custom design. Here there are four different design styles on one chip: Memory banks, data-path units consisting of bit-slice cells, random logic, and PLA blocks.

4.2 Semi-custom Design Methodology

For semi-custom (cell-based) ICs, all of the logic cells are predesigned and possibly all mask layers are customized. Using predesigned cells (standard cells) from a cell library gives designers more opportunities for making better use of the available silicon by removing the constraint of having a fixed structure.

In this design style, all of the commonly used logic cells are developed, characterized, and stored in a standard cell library. A typical library may contain a few hundred cells including inverters, NAND gates, NOR gates, complex AOI, OAI gates, D-latches, and flip-flops. Each gate type can have multiple implementations to provide adequate driving capability for different fanouts. For instance, the inverter gate can have standard size transistors, double size transistors, and quadruple size transistors so that the chip designer can choose the proper size to achieve high circuit speed and layout density. The characterization of each cell consists of delay time vs. load capacitance, circuit simulation model, timing simulation model, fault simulation model, cell data for place-and-route and mask data.

This style makes designers save time, money, and reduce risk by using a predesigned, pretested, and precharacterized standard-cell library. In addition, each standard cell can be optimized individually-each and every transistor in the standard cell can be altered to maximize speed or minimize area. The IC designer defines only the placement of the standard cells and the interconnects in a cell-based IC (CBIC) as shown in Fig.4.2. The disadvantages are the time and expense of designing or buying the standard-cell library, and the time needed to fabricate all layers of the CBIC for each new design.

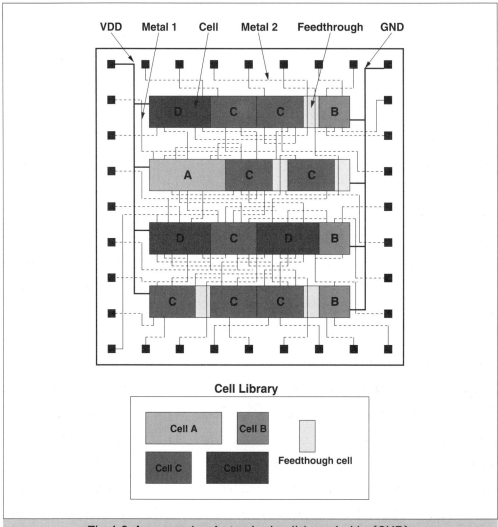

Fig.4.2 An example of standard-cell-based chip (SHR).

4.3 Gate Array Design

Gate arrays (GA) are now very popular since they offer low cost with a fast turn around time. The reason for this is that wafers can be held in stock until they are required, at which point only one or two masks are needed define the interconnections. This saves both time and cost. The use of electronically programmed varieties has grown increasingly popular in prototype development and in short production runs. GAs have been used extensively for replacing random logic in systems which previously would have required a number of printed circuit boards of catalogue parts. In a GA, the transistors are predefined on the silicon wafer. The predefined pattern of transistors on a gate array is the base array, and the smallest element that is replicated to make the base array is the primitive cell. Only the top few layers of metal, which define the interconnect between transistors, are defined by the designer using custom masks. As shown in Fig.4.3(a), using wafers prefabricated up to the metallization steps reduces the time needed to make a GA to a few days or at most a couple of weeks. The costs for all the initial fabrication steps for a GA are shared for each customer, and this reduces the cost of a GA compared to a full-custom or standard-cell ASIC design.

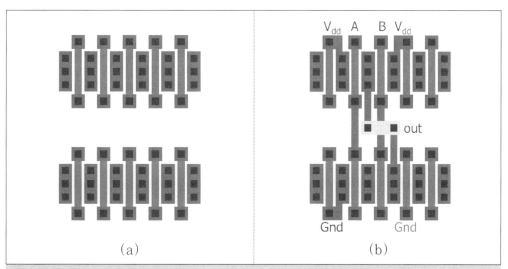

(a)

(b)

Fig.4.3 (a) Prefabricated patterns and (b) 2-input NAND with metal interconnect.

■ Channeled Gate Array

Fig.4.4(a) shows a channeled gate array. The important feature of this type of GA is that only the interconnect is customized by using predefined spaces between rows of the base cells. A channeled gate array is similar to a CBIC–both use rows of cells separated by channels used for interconnect. One difference is that the space for interconnect between rows of cells are fixed in height in a channeled gate array, whereas the space between rows of cells may be adjusted in a CBIC.

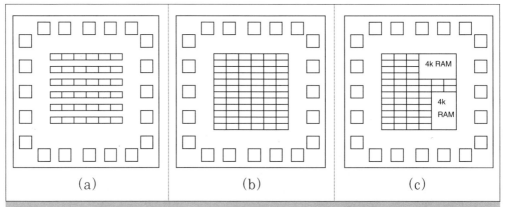

(a)   (b)   (c)

Fig.4.4 (a) A channeled gate-array die. The spaces between rows of the base cells are set aside for interconnect, (b) a channelless gate-array or sea-of-gates (SOG) array, and (c) structured gate array with two memories.

■ Channelless Gate Array

Fig.4.4(b) shows a channelless gate array (also known as a channel-free gate array , or sea-of-gates array). The important feature of this type of GA is that only some (the top few) mask layers are customized. The key difference between a channelless gate array and a channeled gate array is that there are no predefined areas set aside for routing between cells on a channelless gate array. Instead, routing interconnects over the top of the gate-array devices are customized by connecting the contact layer that defines the connections between metal1, the first layer of metal, and the transistors. The logic density-the amount of logic that can be implemented in a given silicon area-is higher for channelless gate arrays than for channeled gate arrays. This is usually attributed to the difference in structures between the two types of arrays. In fact, the difference occurs because the contact mask is customized in a channelless gate array, but is not in a channeled gate array. This leads to denser cells in the channelless architectures.

■ Structured Gate Array

As shown in Fig.4.4(c), an embedded gate array, or structured gate array, combines some of the features of CBICs and MGAs. One of the disadvantages of this MGA is the fixed gate-array base cell. This makes the implementation of memory, for example, difficult and inefficient. In an embedded gate array we set aside some of the IC area and dedicate it to a specific function. This embedded area either can contain a different base cell that is more suitable for building memory cells, or it can contain a complete circuit block, such as a microcontroller. An embedded gate array gives the improved area efficiency and increased performance of a CBIC but with the lower cost and faster turnaround of an MGA. One disadvantage of an embedded gate array is that the embedded function is fixed.

4.4 Field Programmable Gate Array (FPGA)

Fully fabricated FPGA chips containing thousands of logic gates or even more, with programmable interconnects, are available to users for their custom hardware programming. The advantage of FPGA-based design is a very short turn-around time, i.e., the time required from the start of the design process until a functional chip is available. Since no physical manufacturing step is necessary for customizing the FPGA chip, a functional sample can be obtained almost as soon as the design is mapped into a specific technology.

The typical price of FPGA chips are usually higher than other realization alternatives (gate array or standard cells) of the same design, but for small-volume production of ASIC chips and for fast prototyping, FPGA offers a very valuable option. A typical field programmable gate array (FPGA) chip consists of I/O buffers, an array of configurable logic blocks (CLBs), and programmable interconnect structures. The programming of the interconnects is implemented by programming of RAM cells whose output terminals are connected to the gates of MOS pass transistors.

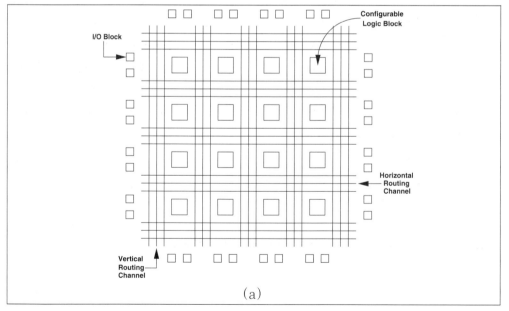

(a)

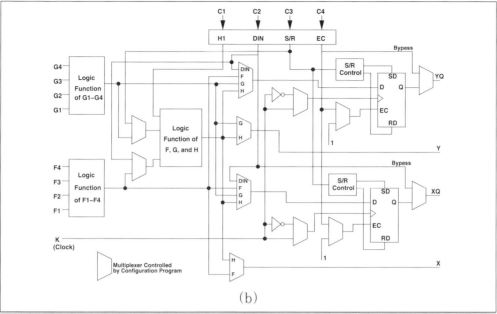

(b)

Fig.4.5 (a) General architecture of Xilinx FPGAs, and (b) XC4000 CLB of the Xilinx FPGA. A general architecture of FPGA from XILINX is shown in Fig.4.5(a) which illustrates the essential characteristics of an FPGA:

ⓐ None of the mask layers are customized.

ⓑ A method for programming the basic logic cells and the interconnect.

ⓒ The core is a regular array of programmable basic logic cells that can implement combinational as well as sequential logic (flip-flops).

ⓓ A matrix of programmable interconnect surrounds the basic logic cells.

ⓔ Programmable I/O cells surround the core.

ⓕ Design turnaround is a few hours.

A CLB (model XC4000 from XILINX) is shown in Fig.4.5(b). It consists of four signal input terminals, a clock signal terminal, user-programmable multiplexers, two SR-latches, and two logic function units for storing the truth table of the Boolean function. The control terminals of multiplexers are not shown explicitly in Fig.4.5(b).

References

[SHR] N. Sherwani, *Algorithms for VLSI Physical Design Automation*, Kluwer Academic Publishers, 1995.

[RUB] Steven M. Rubin, *Computer Aids for VLSI Design*, Second Edition, Addison-Wesley Publishing Company, 1994

[WAE] N.H.E. Weste and K. Eshraghian, *Principles of CMOS VLSI Design*, Addison-Wesley Publishing Company, Second Edition, 1993.

LAB3. 4-Bit Ripple Carry Adder Design I

In this lab, you will draw a 4-bit ripple carry adder (RCA) layout using MyChip A schematic hierarchy of this design is shown in Fig.L3.1. You'll design the RCA and extract its parameter (netlist), and finally simulate the netlist using MySPICE.

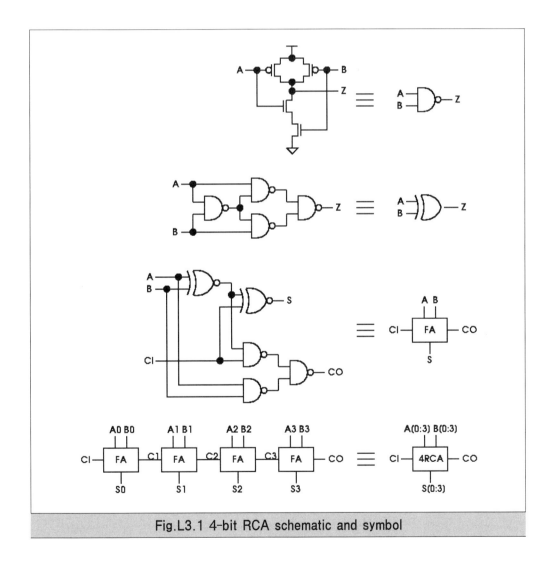

Fig.L3.1 4-bit RCA schematic and symbol

Before designing the RCA, design a one-bit full adder (FA). Label the input data as A, B, and CI, and the output as S and CO. Use MyChip cell hierarchy to design the FA. In order to simplify the layout, use three 2-input nand cells and two 2-input exclusive-or (XOR) cells as subcells in this lab. And XOR can be implemented using 4 nand cells as shown in Fig.L3.1. The top-level parent cell, FA, will contain five children cells, nand_0, nand_1, nand_2, xor_0, and xor_1. When using cell hierarchy in MyCAD, make sure that the labels, **A, B, CI, S**, and **CO**, are placed on a square of paint contained in the top-level parent cell, **FA**. Then, using four FA cells, design a 4-bit RCA. Make sure that the labels of this RCA are A0~A3, B0~B3, CI, S0~S3, and CO.

STEP 1 Design of Cells-NAND2, XOR2, FA, and RCA

The following shows the steps of designing the cells using stick diagrams:

ⓐ Design the NAND and XOR gates whose stick diagram are in Fig.L3.2. Make sure that the height of the cells are the same (《 110λ), and make the cells as small as possible. In this example, XOR consists of 4 NAND cells. Use metal2 and via layers for connecting vertical nets to avoid shorting wires. Note that you need to check the functionality of your XOR gate with MySPICE when you finish the layouts.

ⓑ Design the FA in Fig.L3.3. Open a new structure and save as new name (FA). Put two instances of XOR gates and three instances of NAND gates on the new cell as shown in Fig.L3.3.

Now flip the second XOR gate vertically and then horizontally. Then, merge all the cells. Note that the routing process only shows connectivity of cells in Fig.L3.2, thus you should compact your layout keeping minimum sizes and shortest paths.

ⓒ Design an RCA as shown in Fig.L3.4. Place 4 instances of the FA on a new cell (RCA), and route the RCAs. Make sure the labels are only on this top level schematic (RCA).

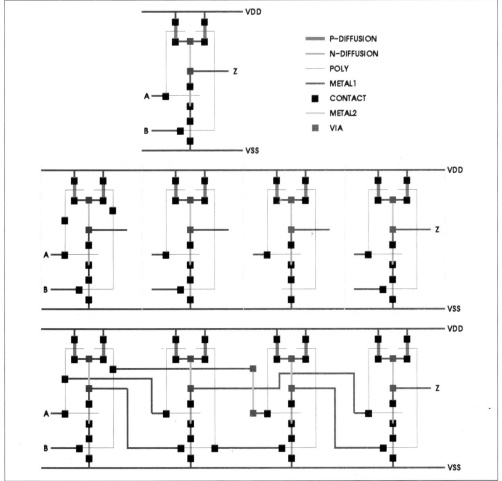

Fig.L3.2 Stick diagrams of NAND and the legend of this stick diagram (Top), 4 NAND cells (Middle), and XOR gate (Bottom).

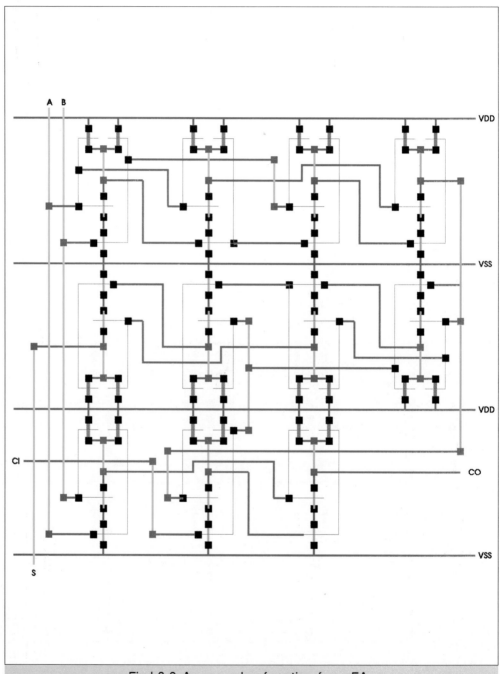

Fig.L3.3 An example of routing for a FA.

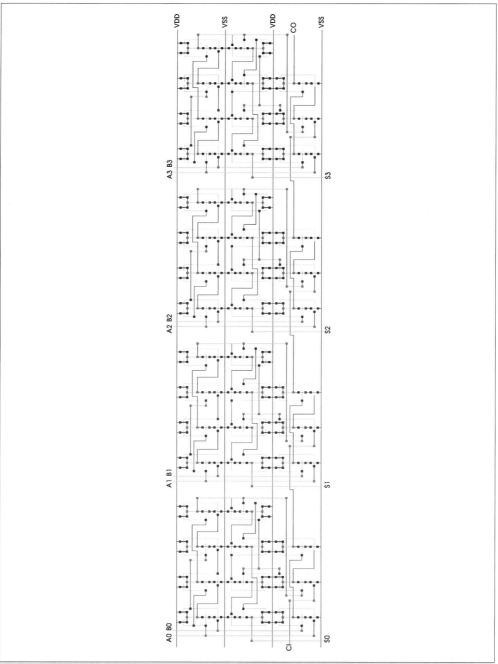

Fig.L3.4 An example of routing for a 4-bit RCA

STEP 2 | Running MySPICE

The simulation procedure is the same that of Lab2 except for a different CUT (FA and RCA) and a different input file (.cir).

ⓐ Extract Netlists: FA and RCA from MyChip.
ⓑ Run MySPICE for RA and RCA.

Question

Is there another way to implement a CMOS XOR gate?

Chapter V. CMOS Layout Styles

5.1 | Primitive Cell Design

5.1.1 Standard Cell

The layout for a MOS transistor pair is presented in Fig.5.1(a). In this layout, the connection in the source region is implemented by abutment. In this way, an even number of PMOS or NMOS can be implemented by mirroring the initial pair, as represented in Fig.5.1(b). In Fig.5.1(b), the connection in the drain region is implemented with contacts.

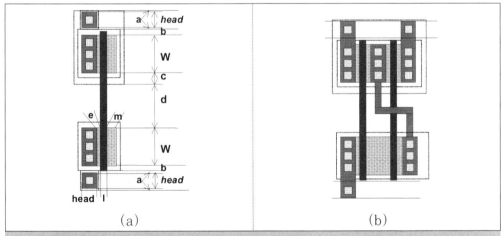

(a)   (b)

Fig.5.1 Examples of CMOS Layout: (a) Transistor pair and (b) NAND gate

The size of a primitive cell is determined by lower level contacted metal pitch (MP), which is the width of the via/contact plus the spacing between the via and the adjacent line as shown in Fig.5.2. The area of a 2-input NAND cell is typically 4 MPs in width by 16 MPs in height. Each standard cell in a library is rectangular with the same height but have different widths. The bounding box (BB, not shown in Fig.5.1) of a logic cell is the smallest rectangle that encloses all of the geometry of the cell. The BB of a cell is normally determined by the well layers. Cell connectors or terminals (the logical connectors) must be placed on the cell abutment box (BB, not shown in Fig.5.1). The physical connector must normally overlap the abutment box slightly, usually by at least 1λ to assure connection without leaving a tiny space between the ends of the two wires. The standard cells are constructed so they can all be placed next to each other horizontally with the cell BBs touching. And Fig.5.3 shows the components of a standard cell.

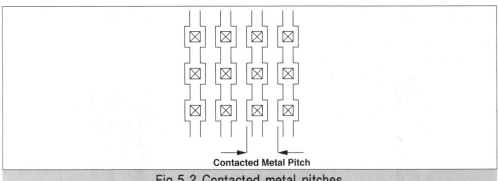

Fig.5.2 Contacted metal pitches

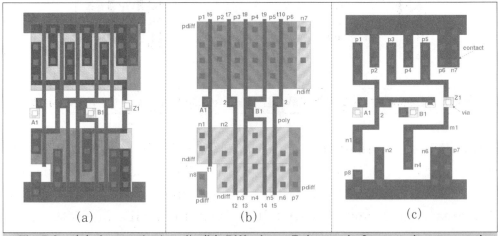

Fig.5.3   (a) A standard cell (b) Diffusion, Poly, and Contact layers, and (c) M1 and Contact layers [MJS]

5.1.2 *Datapath Cell*

Fig.5.4 shows a datapath flip-flop. The primary, thicker, power buses run vertically on M2 with thinner, internal power running horizontally on M1. The control signals (clock in this case) run vertically through the cell on M2. The control signals that are common to the cells above and below are connected directly in M2. The other signals (data, q, and qbar in this example) are brought out to the wiring channel between the rows of datapath cells.

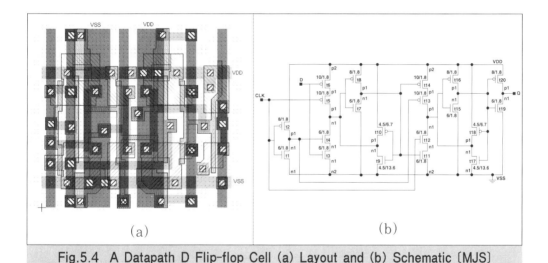

(a) (b)

Fig.5.4 A Datapath D Flip-flop Cell (a) Layout and (b) Schematic [MJS]

This flip-flop uses a pair of cross-coupled inverters for storage in both the master and slave latches. This leads to a smaller and potentially faster layout than the flip-flop circuits that we use in gate-array and standard-cell ASIC libraries. The device sizes of the inverters in the data-path flip-flops are adjusted so that the state of the latches may be changed. Normally using this type of circuit is dangerous in an uncontrolled environment. However, because the datapath structure is regular and known, the parasitic capacitances that affect the operation of the logic cell are also known. This is another advantage of the datapath structure.

5.2 | I/O Cell (Pad)

The circuitry on a particular chip has to connect with other circuits. These may be chips, display devices, transducers or electro-mechanical devices; the capacitance connected to the chip could be very large and become a problem. In some cases, the devices being driven will require or supply TTL signal levels. In others, they may be liable to short circuits, have high noise levels or be prone to discharge spikes of several kV. Each of these situations will require the imposition of circuitry to interface the chip to the external environment. Most IC designers avoid the problem of pad design and take pad drivers from standard libraries.

Pads are connected to the pins of the package with bonding wires. The pad is often used also to include the circuitry that is used to interface the CMOS logic within the IC to the outside world. At least two pads in each circuit will be used to connect the chip to the VDD and VSS power supply lines, while other pads will be used for input and output connections. Some pads may also be required to be bi-directional. In such cases, there is usually a control connection to determine the direction of signal transfer. An important function for all pad driver circuitry is the protection of the chip circuitry against destruction due to over-voltage pulses. These may be due to electrostatic discharges or due to faults on other circuitry that cause unexpectedly high voltages to be applied to the chip pins.

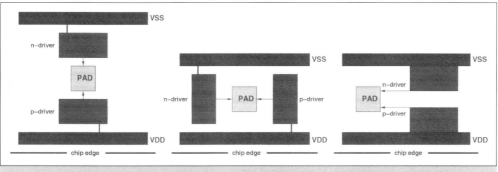

Fig.5.5 Pads and associated circuitry [WAE].

Typical arrangements for pads and associated circuitry are shown in Fig.5.5. Bonding pads are normally positioned near the chip edge, although there is often a VDD bus between the bonding pads and the chip boundary. Pad circuitry is almost invariably designed so that the various circuit blocks have standard physical sizes and provide regular spacing of the bond pads around the chip when the blocks are abutted.

5.2.1 Input Pad

Input pads always contain over-voltage protection features. They can also contain inverting circuitry or Schmitt trigger circuitry if the input signals to be fed to the circuit are not known to be proper CMOS level signals. The capacitance of the gate is very small, so sufficient electrostatic charge can easily be accumulated to produce a voltage high enough to cause failure of the input transistor. With modern processes, a voltage of only about 30 V or so is required to break down the thin gate oxide, although experiments have shown that failure is often caused by non-uniform current flow producing current densities that give thermal breakdown first. The action of walking across a synthetic carpet can give an individual a potential of 15 kV, so the first precaution is obviously to try to prevent electrostatic charge coming into contact with the chip pins. It is normally recommended that electrostatic kits with earthed mats and wrist straps are used for handling CMOS devices, but this is still not an adequate safeguard because of the minute charge required. The usual protection circuit consists of a resistance and diode clamps, as shown in Fig.5.6.

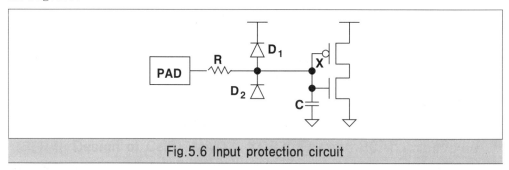

Fig.5.6 Input protection circuit

D1 will turn on if the voltage at X rises significantly above VDD; similarly, D2 clamps the potential close to VSS if X is driven negative. The resistor R is normally a poly-silicon track of about 1KW and this is used to limit the maximum current that can flow through the diodes (in the event of the diode turning on) to a non-destructive level. Modern designs tend to make use of a diffused resistor (for example, p-type diffusion in an n-well) even though this carries with it the risk of inducing latch-up. As an alternative, a poly-silicon resistor may be used (although it occupies more space); the thick field oxide isolation guards against the possibility of charge injection.

The presence of the diodes reduces the input resistance of the circuit to $\sim 10^{10}\Omega$. This is not likely to be important, but the effect of the protection structure on the speed of the circuit may be significant.

The 1 kW resistor and the input capacitance of the first stage of the circuit will present an RC time-constant. If this time constant is unacceptable, the value of the resistor can be reduced, which reduces the voltage capability of the protection circuit. Protection circuits should have a capability of about 2 kV. A capability of 8 kV is possible without unreasonable degradation of the speed of the circuit when careful design techniques are used.

5.2.2 *Output Pad*

Output pads must be capable of providing relatively large currents to off-chip wiring, and perhaps to the inputs of several other devices. The typical off-chip capacitance (C_L) is typically 15 pF. Once this value is determined, the pad can be optimally driven by a cascaded chain of repeaters where each stage in the output pad gets larger by a factor of a_{opt} which is determined by examining two things: the ratio (Y) of C_L to the input capacitance of a minimum-sized inverter in the given process technology, and the ratio (γ) of intrinsic device output capacitance to input capacitance, or $C_{junction} / C_{in}$. After calculating these two ratios, the optimal tapering factor should be determined recursively by using the following equation:

$$a_{opt} = e^{\frac{\gamma + a_{opt}}{a_{opt}}}$$

Subsequently, a_{opt} can be used to find the optimal number of repeaters in the cascaded chain, N_{opt}.

$$N_{opt} = \frac{\ln Y}{\ln a_{opt}}$$

Then, N_{opt} is rounded down to the nearest even integer (N), so as to remain non-inverting. Thus, N is re-evaluated as the scaling factor a:

$$a = Y^{1/n}$$

Drivers are typically composed of logic inverters with high current driving capability. Often an even number of inverters may be connected in cascade if a non-inverting driver structure is required. In Fig.5.7, for instance, an output pad driver with $a=3$, N=4, and γ =0.5 is shown, and the total capacitance is $1.72C_L$.

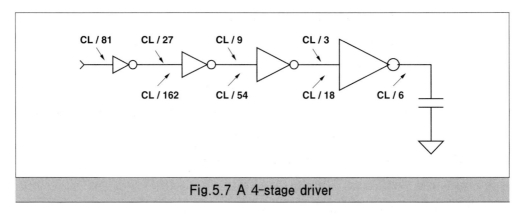

Fig.5.7 A 4-stage driver

5.2.3 Bi-directional Pads

Fig.5.8 shows a three-state bi-directional output buffer. When the output enable (OE) signal is high, the circuit functions as a non-inverting buffer driving the value of DATAin onto the I/O pad. When OE is low, the output transistors or drivers, M1 and M2, are disconnected. This allows multiple drivers to be connected on a bus. It is up to the designer to make sure that a bus never has two drivers—a problem known as contention.

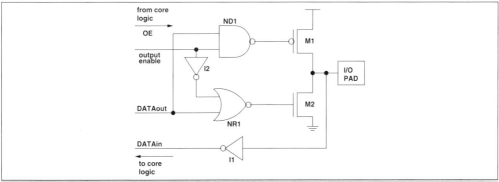

Fig.5.8 A three-state bi-directional output buffer. When the output enable, OE, is '1' the output section is enabled and drives the I/O pad. When OE is '0' the output buffer is placed in a high-impedance state.

In order to prevent the problem opposite of contention, a bus floating to an intermediate voltage when there are no bus drivers, a bus keeper or bus-hold cell can be used. A bus keeper normally acts like two weak (low drive-strength) cross-coupled inverters that act as a latch to retain the last logic state on the bus. The latch is design to be weak enough so that it can be driven easily to the opposite state. Even though bus keepers act like latches, they should not be used as latches, since their drive strength is weak.

5.3 An Example of Physical Design: SRAM Design

For another example of designing a chip, let's follow the construction process of a static-memory chip [LYN][RUB]. This chip makes use of a novel four-transistor bit of static memory. The fundamental memory cell is logically designed using the schematic environment (Fig.5.9(a)). An equivalent CMOS layout is then produced without concern for compact spacing (Fig.5.9(b)). For proper layout efficiency, alternate bits of memory are different, so two bits define the leaf cell of the design. These bits can be compacted by the one-dimensional compacter (Fig.5.9(c)), and then compacted further by rearranging components and re-compacting (Fig.5.9(d)).

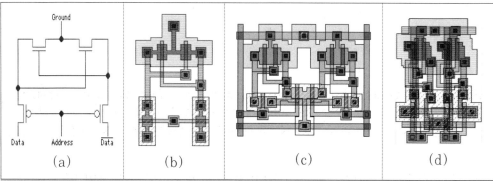

(a)   (b)   (c)   (d)

Fig.5.9 (a) Schematic for four-transistor static-memory cell. (b) CMOS layout for four-transistor static-memory cell. (c) CMOS layout for two four-transistor static-memory cells. And (d) compacted CMOS layout for two four-transistor static-memory cells.

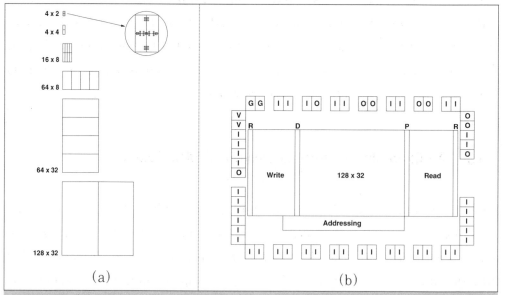

(a)   (b)

Fig.5.10 (a) Hierarchical organization for 128 × 32 array of static-memory cells. And (b) Floor-plan of static-memory chip.

To create a 128 × 32-bit array of memory, six levels of hierarchy are employed to build a 4 × 2 array, a 4 × 4 array, a 16 × 8 array, a 64 × 8 array, a 64 × 32 array, and a 128 × 32 array (see Fig.5.10 (a)). Note that each level of hierarchy actually connects its subcells with little stitches so that the overall connectivity is maintained. These stitches are automatically created by the router. Also, each level of hierarchy must export all unstitched ports to the next level.

Once the basic memory array is created, driving circuitry must be placed on the edges. A word (32-bit) driver for a single word is designed to match the pitch of the memory, and the driver is arranged using hierarchy. The block of 128 drivers attaches to the bottom of the memory array. Similar drivers and decoders are built on the sides. The overall floor-plan, including the pads, is shown in Fig.5.10(b). This layout contains 32,650 transistors, described with 110 cells.

References

[MJS] Michael John Sebastian and John Smith, Application-Specific Integrated Circuits, Wesley Publishing Company, 1997.

[WAE] N.H.E. Weste and K. Eshraghian, Principles of CMOS VLSI Design, Second Edition, Addison-Wesley Publishing Company, 1992.

[LYN] Lyon, Richard F. and Schediwy, Richard R., "CMOS Static Memory with a New Four-Transistor Memory Cell," Proceedings Stanford Conference on Advanced Research in VLSI (Losleben, ed), 111-132, March 1987.

[RUB] Steven M. Rubin, Computer Aids for VLSI Design, Second Edition, Addison-Wesley Publishing Company, 1994

LAB4. 4-Bit Ripple Carry Adder Design II

In this lab, you will draw another 4-bit ripple carry adder (RCA) layout using the full adder (FA) as shown in Fig.L4.1. First, draw the stick diagram for this FA, and then create the cell using MyCAD. Then, using four FA cells, design a 4-bit RCA. Make sure that the labels of this RCA are A0~A3, B0~B3, CI, S0~S3, and CO.

After parameter extraction, you'll simulate the netlist using MySPICE as in Lab3. Before designing the RCA, design a one-bit full adder (FA) as one circuit. Label the input data as A, B, and CI, and the output as S and CO. When using cell hierarchy in MyCAD, make sure that the labels, **A, B, CI, S**, and **CO**, are placed on a square of paint contained in the top-level parent cell, **FA**. Then, using four FA cells, design a 4-bit RCA. Make sure that the labels of this RCA are A0~A3, B0~B3, CI, S0~S3, and CO.

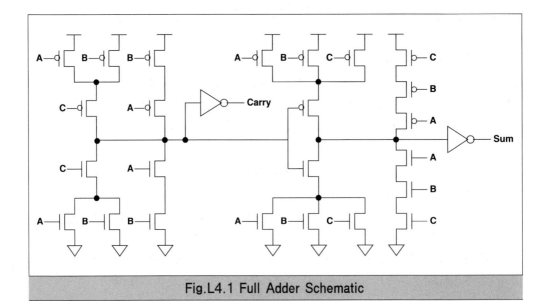

Fig.L4.1 Full Adder Schematic

Chapter VI. Routing Techniques and Algorithms

6.1 Routing Styles

Once the designer has floorplanned a chip and the logic cells within the flexible blocks have been placed, it is time to make the connections by routing the chip. The space between these cells can be as simple as a rectangle as shown in Fig.6.1(a).

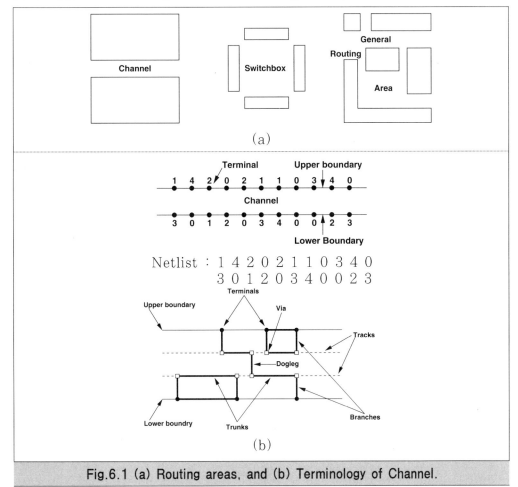

(a)

(b)

Fig.6.1 (a) Routing areas, and (b) Terminology of Channel.

When the routing space is rectangular and contains connection points on two facing sides, it is called a channel. When routing is done on all four sides of a rectangular area, it is called a switchbox. More complex routing areas usually need to be decomposed into channels and switchboxes. Many different techniques exist for routing, depending on the number of wires to run, the complexity of the routing space, and the number of layers available for crossing. Fig.6.1(b) represents the terminology of channel.

Fig.6.2 illustrates some routing layer models. According to the number of layers and the process steps, routing layer models are represented as VH, HV, VHV, or HVH model, where V and H stand for vertical and horizontal respectively.

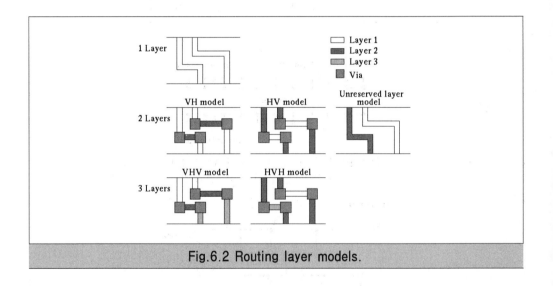

Fig.6.2 Routing layer models.

6.1.1 Channel-based routing vs. Area-based routing

In Fig.6.3(a), net 1 is above net 2 in the first column of the channel. Thus net 1 imposes a vertical constraint on net 2. Net 2 is above net 1 in the last column of the channel. Then net 2 also imposes a vertical constraint on net 1. It is impossible to route this arrangement using two routing layers with the restriction of using only one trunk for each net. If the vertical-constraint graph for this situation is constructed as shown in Fig.6.3(b), there is a loop or cycle between nets 1 and 2. If there is any such vertical-constraint cycle between two or more nets, this routing will fail. A dogleg router removes the restriction that each net can use only one track or trunk. Fig.6.3(c) shows how adding a dogleg permits a channel with a vertical-constraint cycle to be routed.

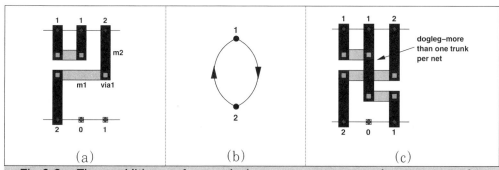

Fig.6.3 The addition of a dogleg, an extra trunk, can resolve vertical-constraint cycles in the wiring of a net.

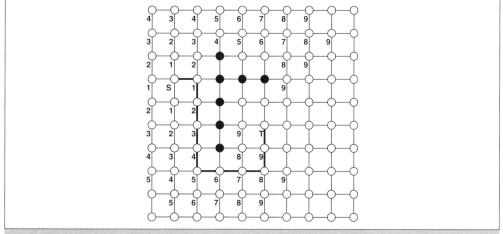

Fig.6.4 The Lee maze-running algorithm.

Area-based routing assumes that cell placement is fixed, and it does its best to complete the route within a known area and die size. Fig.6.4 illustrates, for example, the Lee maze-running algorithm. The algorithm finds a path from source (S) to target (T) and represents the routing layer as a grid, where each gridpoint can contain connections to adjacent gridpoints. It searches for a shortest-path connection between the source and target nodes by performing a breadth-first search and labeling each gridpoint with its distance from the source. This expansion phase will eventually reach the target node if a connection is possible. A second traceback phase then forms the connection by following any path with decreasing labels. This algorithm is guaranteed to find the shortest path between a source and destination for a given connection. However, when multiple connections are made one connection may block other connections. The algorithm is often called wave propagation because it sends out waves, which spread out like those created by dropping a stone into a pond.

6.1.2 Gridded vs. Gridless Routing

It is clear that variable width and spacing is required to address the deep submicron effects of noise, crosstalk and EM. A gridded router increases spacing by the increment of routing grids as shown in Fig.6.5. A gridless router, on the other hand, can increase spacing by only the specified amount. This amount does not need to be an increment of routing grids.

In gridded routing, the routing area is divided into a uniform grid for every metal layer. This is equal to the width plus spacing for that metal layer. All the wires on any metal layer should use one grid or a whole integer multiple of the grid for routing any wire. The main advantage of gridded routing is that very large designs can be handled. One disadvantage is that variable width and spacing may not be handled as efficiently as gridless routing. Gridded routing is widely used by inside-the-block or standard-cell routers due to its large capacity.

A gridless routing is a shape-based or object-based routing that views pins, wires and blockages as objects and routes around them without a routing grid. The advantage of a gridless routing is that it gives the user complete control over wire width and spacing. Gridless routing can also handle blocks with different pin pitches, thereby making it easier to route blocks with different physical characteristics (such as intellectual property blocks) in a given SoC design. The main disadvantage of a gridless routing, is that it can only handle a limited number of objects or shapes. Therefore, gridless routers are mainly used for top level routing or interblock routing.

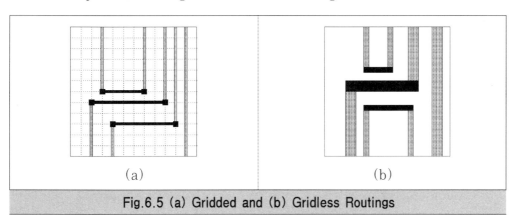

(a)   (b)

Fig.6.5 (a) Gridded and (b) Gridless Routings

6.2 Routing Area Minimization Techniques

The basic requirements for an efficient VLSI design is to satisfy the performance needs of a specific system within a minimum area. As the number of devices increase, the number of interconnections as well as the area used for these interconnections also increase. However, additional layers for interconnections are being made available for designers to allow for more compact systems. The only area outside a channel in a Standard Cell Design is the area over the cell and this technique is called Over-the-Cell-Routing.

Vias are unavoidable if more than one layer is used for routing, however, minimizing the number of vias is desirable for the following reasons:

⓪ In integrated circuit fabrication, the yield is inversely proportional to the number of vias. A chip with more vias has a smaller probability of being fabricated correctly.

⓫ Every via has an associated resistance (more than the layers it is connecting) which affects the circuit performance.

⓬ The size of the via is usually larger than the width of the wires. As a result vias increase routing space (creating the so called bumps).

⓭ Completion rate of routing is also inversely related to the number of vias [SHR].

⓮ Some improvement is also achievable by choosing a correct location for a via within a routing channel. This technique is called Via Shifting.

6.2.1 *Over the Cell (OTC) Routing*

To decrease the area consumed in a routing channel within a given technology, it is only possible if some of the routing is done outside of the channel thus decreasing the number of connections within the channel. This is only possible if the area over the cells can be utilized for cell interconnections. Using two-layer routing, if the logic cells do not contain any M2, it is possible to complete some routing in M2 using over-the-cell (OTC) routing. With three or more levels of metal routing, it is possible to reduce the channel height in a row-based ASIC to zero. All of the interconnect is then completed over the cell. Over the cell routing first concentrates on using the M2 layer over the cell for routing. Simple algorithms divide the problem into three steps [CON]:

ⓐ Routing over the cells in a planar fashion.
ⓑ Choosing net segments in the channel.
ⓒ Routing the channel.

The first step reduces the number of connections in the channel and contributes to a decreased channel height (See Fig.6.6).

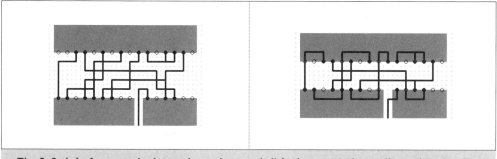

Fig.6.6 (a) A normal channel routing and (b) the over the cell routing for the above routing solution

6.2.2 *Via Shifting*

Vias provide the connection between two routing layers. A via usually occupies a larger area than the minimum width of the tracks (Fig.6.7). Thus a track with a via has a bump which is wider than the remaining track. Thus, careful assignments of vias along the track may reduce the overall channel height and decrease the area consumed for routing.

In [YNG], Yang and Wong studied algorithms for efficient via shifting. For most modern technologies, two layers are used for routing-one for the horizontal and the other for the vertical movements. This produces a large number of vias as each direction change needs a via. It is shown that in typical routing, the vias have some freedom to move along the nets without violating the design rules.

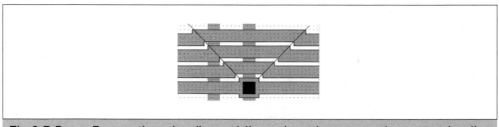

Fig.6.7 Bump Propagation, the diagonal lines show the propagation expansion line

An algorithm is proposed in which the movements of vias are classified, and the designer tries to distribute the vias equally under the columns. In [PTR], a general channel compaction algorithm which incorporates a couple of different compaction methods is proposed. The initial input undergoes a via minimization algorithm, to ensure that all unnecessary vias are removed. The new solution is then compacted downward. Beginning from the bottom, all tracks are pulled as close together as the design rules permit. This results in a layout where tracks have a lot of jogs, which can be removed with a classical straightening algorithm. The algorithm takes the bump propagation into account and tries to shift the vias out of the critical path, where it generates the movement space with left and right compactions iteratively.

6.2.3 Via Minimization

There are two main approaches for via minimization. The constrained via minimization (CVM) tries to minimize the number of vias within a finished design. The CVM is also called the layer assignment problem because it tries to determine which net segments will be on which layer. The algorithm here is based on [HSU]. The second approach is the unconstrained via minimization, also called the topological via minimization (TVM), tries to find a topology for a given connection matrix with the minimum number of vias.

CVM algorithms concentrate on minimizing the number of vias in a given routing system. They do not change the routing topology, they only reduce the number of vias. But there might be other routing solutions for the same problem, which may not be achieved by CVM algorithms. The main philosophy of TVM is based on this idea. The main problem of TVM is that it ignores net length and channel height.

For each cluster there are two assignment solutions. All the connecting segments can only be flipped over from a specified initial condition. First, a Cluster Graph is defined where the edges are defined as the weight (w) of the cluster which is calculated from $w(e) = 2q-p$, where p is the number of via candidates between the incident cluster and q is the number of vias introduced by the known (partial) solution. The number of vias that can be reduced by flipping a set of E clusters is equal to the total number of edges that do not connect members of E.

■ Constrained Via Minimization (CVM)

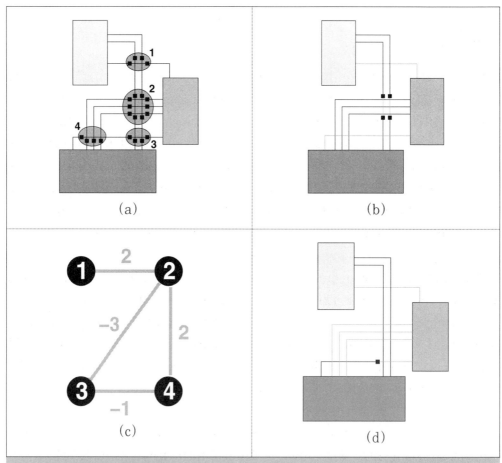

Fig.6.8 (a) Via candidates and clusters for a given routing, (b) A Partial routing solution, 4 Vias, (c) Cluster Graph, and (d) a solution with only one via

The allowable flips are as follows:

1	= 2	
2	= 1	
3	= 1	
4	= -4	
1-2	= -1	
1-3	= 3	*
1-4	= -2	
2-3	= -4	
2-4	= 3	*
3-4	= -1	
1-2-3	= -4	
1-2-4	= 1	
1-3-4	= 1	
2-3-4	= 2	

This displays that flipping clusters 2-3 or 1-4 will reduce the number of vias by 3.

Topological Via Minimization (TVM)

Topological Via Minimization was first introduced by Hsu [HSU]. Subsets of the general problem such as two terminal nets, were proved to be NP hard and algorithms were developed to find routing solutions. In topological via minimization the main goal is to reduce the vias at the expense of longer wires and denser channels Fig.6.9 is often used in work related to the TVM. All the remaining wires are forced around the via enabling a layout with only one via. This example is frequently used to display the shortcomings of the TVM. The very same routing could be realized in much less area if two vias were used, as shown in Fig.6.9(c).

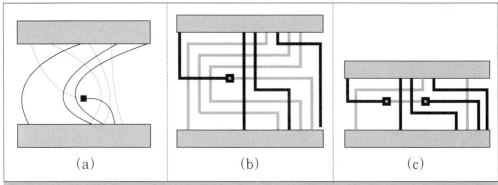

(a)	(b)	(c)

Fig.6.9 (a) Routing nets around a via, (b) Routing 7 tracks around a via, and (c) 3 tracks around 2 vias

6.3 │ Special Routings

6.3.1 Clock Routing

Ideally, clock signals should have minimum rise and fall times, specified duty cycles, and zero skew. In reality, clock signals have nonzero skews and noticeable rise and fall times; duty cycles can also vary. In fact, as much as 10% of a machine cycle time is expended to allow realistic clock skews in large computer systems. However, the generated clock signal can be quite process-dependent and unstable.

Since clock signals are required almost uniformly over the chip area, it is desirable that all clock signals are distributed with a uniform delay. Several distribution networks are shown in Fig.6.10 according to types of clock phase and constraint. Regardless of the exact geometry of the clock distribution network, the clock signals must be buffered in multiple stages as shown in Fig.6.11 to handle the high fan-out loads. It is also essential that every buffer-stage drives the same number of fan-out gates so that the clock delays are always balanced.

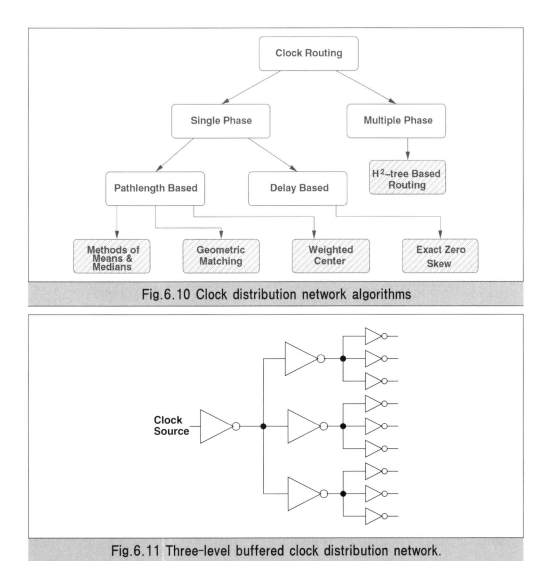

Fig.6.10 Clock distribution network algorithms

Fig.6.11 Three-level buffered clock distribution network.

■ The Method of Means and Medians(MMM)

The MMM algorithm follows a top-down method. The MMM algorithm recursively partitions a circuit into two parts and then connects the center of masses of the two sub-circuits.

ⓐ The region S is partitioned into two subregions S_L and S_R, with an equal number of points.

ⓑ The center of mass is computed for each subregion.

ⓒ The center of mass in the region S is connected to each of the centers of masses in the subregions S_L and S_R.

ⓓ The subregions S_L and S_R are then recursively split in the Y-direction.

ⓔ Steps b-e are repeated with alternate splitting in the X- and Y-directions.

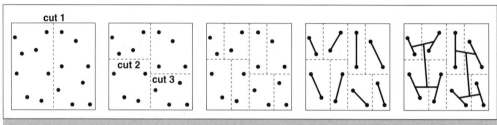

Fig.6.12 The method of Means and Medians [JCK].

■ The Geometric Matching Algorithm

In this approach the clock routing is achieved by constructing a binary tree using recursive geometric matching.

ⓐ A bottom-up method based on recursive matching

ⓑ Compute a minimal length matching on the set of sinks and connect each pair by a segment.

ⓒ The tapping point for each subtree is the point on the segment such that the clock skew of the subtree is minimized.

ⓓ The above steps are repeated on the set of tapping points recursively.

ⓔ Apply H-flipping to handle edge intersection and to further reduce clock skew.

134

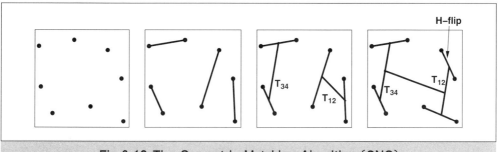

Fig.6.13 The Geometric Matching Algorithm [CNG]

◼ Exact Zero Skew Algorithm

An example with eight clock pins (Fig.6.14(a)) is used to illustrate the algorithm.

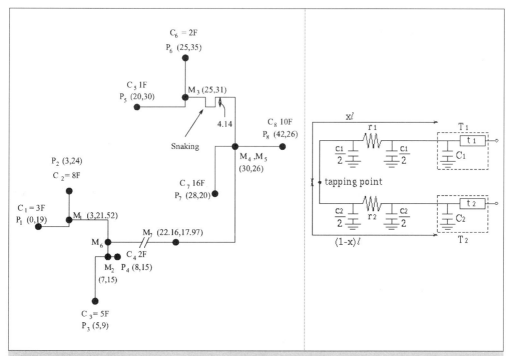

Fig.6.14 (a) A zero skew wiring result of a simple example and (b) A zero skew merge of two subtrees [TSY]

ⓐ To ensure the delay from the tapping point to the leaf nodes of subtrees T_1 and T_2 (Fig.6.14(b)) are equal, it requires that

$$(xl) \times r_1 \left(\frac{c_1}{2} + c_1 \right) + t_1 = (1-x) l \times \left(r_2 \left(\frac{c_2}{2} + c_2 \right) \right) + t_2$$

ⓑ Solving the above equation,

$$x = \frac{(t_2 - t_1) + al \left(c_2 + \frac{c_2}{2} \right)}{al(\beta l + c_1 + c_2)}$$

, where a and β are the resistance and capacitance per unit length of wire and l is the length of the interconnecting wire. ($\gamma_1 = al$, $\gamma_2 = \beta l$)

■ Weighted Center Algorithm

ⓐ A bottom-up method (Fig.6.15).

ⓑ Connect each port pair of segments and compute a center between the pair.

ⓒ Connect each pair of the above centers and compute the center distance from the port of the segment recursively.

ⓓ Compute the centers with the equal-distance from the root to the port of the segment and connect the centers to the root.

■ The H-Tree Based Algorithm

A symmetrical H structure is duplicated across the chip (Fig.6.16). This way the different chip components are equidistant from the clock entry point. This thereby minimizes skew.

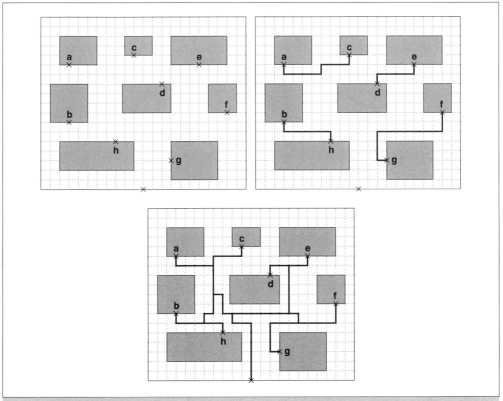

Fig.6.15 Weighted Center.

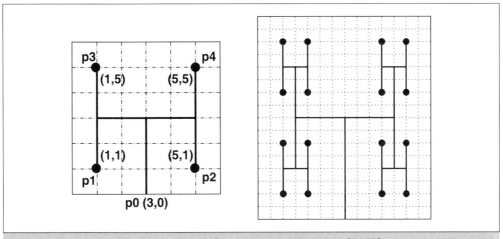

Fig.6.16 The H-Tree Based Algorithm (DHR).

6.3.2 Power Routing

IC power distribution systems provide voltages and currents to the logic functions of a chip. Because of their importance, supply voltages must be constant across a chip, and must be reliable throughout the chip's lifetime. In DSM devices, however, power and ground lines may fluctuate because of increased resistance of metal nets, high current levels and pin inductance. In addition, the narrow widths of power nets in DSM devices can reduce reliability. As a result, power systems have become so complex that they can no longer be routed using standard routing techniques. The complexity of power distribution grids has a significant effect on a device's performance. The resistance of power lines can cause voltage drops. These affect noise margins, which then affect the chip's timing and function. High currents can also cause EM effects in which metal lines deteriorate over a chip's lifetime.

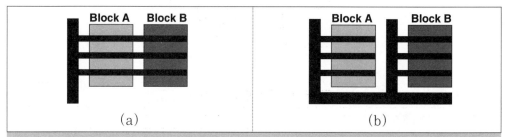

Fig.6.17 Examples of Power Routing: (a) through a block, and (b) around blocks.

Routing through blocks must be done carefully to avoid voltage drops as the current passes through blocks in series. Routing around blocks and I/O rings can ensure even power distribution, but requires wide wires that consume valuable real estate. Ideally, the main trunks should be large enough to handle all the current flowing through separate branches. However, large power busses employ T-junctions (Fig.6.15(b)) that have a high current density and may be prone to EM problems. Each of the power buses has to be sized according to the current it will carry. Too much current in a power bus can lead to a failure through a mechanism known as EM. The required power-bus widths can be estimated using a separate power simulation. Thus, many designers put the power grid in higher layers of metal and use vias to distribute power.

For a direct current (DC) the mean time to failure (MTTF) due to EM is experimentally found to obey the following equation:

$$MTTF = A J^{-2} \exp -E/kT,$$

where J is the current density; E is approximately 0.5eV; k, Boltzmann's constant, is $8.62*10^{-5}$ eVK^{-1}; and T is the absolute temperature in kelvins.

References

[SHR] N. Sherwani, Algorithms for VLSI Physical Design Automation, *Kluwer Academic Publishers*, pp. 345, 1995.

[CON] J. Cong, J.L. Liu, "Over the cell channel routing", *IEEE Transactions on Computer Aided Design*, pp. 408, 1990.

[YNG] Cai Yang, D.F. Wong, "Efficient via shifting algorithms in channel compaction", *IEEE Transactions on CAD of Integrated Circuits and Systems*, Dec 1993, pp. 1848 -1857.

[PTR] R.Y. Pinter, "Optimal layer assignment for interconnect", *Proceedings of IEEE International Conference on Circuits and Computers"*, pp. 382, Sep 1982.

[HSU] C.P. Hsu, "Minimum-via topological routing", *IEEE Transactions on CAD of Integrated Circuits and Systems*, pp.235, 1983.

[JCK] Jackson, Srinivasan, and Kuh, "Clock Routing for High-Performance ICs", DAC, 1990.

[CNG] Cong, Kahng, and Robins, "Matching-based Models for High-Performance Clock Routing", *IEEE TCAD*, 1993.

[DHR] Dhar, Franklin, and Wang, "Reduction of Clock Delays in VLSIStructure", *ICCAD*, 1984

[TSY] Tasy, "Exact Zero Skew Algorithm", *ICCAD*, 1991

LAB5. Various XOR Implementations

Pre-Lab: Dynamic Logic and Transmission Gate

The dynamic logic uses a sequence of precharge and conditional evaluation phases to realize complex logic functions with less transistors. Consider Fig.L5.1(a). When CLK is low (0), the output node Z is precharged to VDD by a PMOS transistor. During that time, the NMOS connected to GND is off. Thus, no DC current flows regardless of the values of the input signals. On the other hand, when CLK is high (1), the precharge PMOS is OFF, and the evaluation NMOS is turned ON. Depending on the values of the inputs and the composition of the pull-down network, a conditional path between Z and GND is created. If such a path exists, the output Z is discharged, and a low output signal is obtained. If not, the precharged value remains on the output node. Several important features of the dynamic gate are following:

1. The logic function is implemented by the NMOS pull-down network.
2. The number of transistors for dynamic logic is N+2 versus 2N for static CMOS.
3. Due to the reduced number of transistors per gate and the single transistors load per fan-in, the load capacitance for this gate is substantially lower than for static CMOS. This results in faster switching speeds.
4. It consumes only dynamic power.

Another promising approach to implementing complex logic is to realize it as a logical network of transmission gates as shown in Fig.L5.1(b). The Transmission Gate (TG) approach has the advantage of being simple and fast. Complex CMOS combinational logic is implemented with a minimal number of transistors. This reduces the parasitic capacitances and results in a faster circuit. This gate is composed of an NMOS transistor and a PMOS device in a parallel arrangement. The TG acts as a bi-directional switch controlled by the gate signals; B and BB for Fig.L5.1(b). When B = 0, and BB = 1, both transistors in the upper TG are on, allowing the signal to pass through the gate. On the other hand, the transistors in the lower TG are OFF. When B =1, and BB = 0, the upper TG is in cutoff and the lower TG is ON.

Design of XOR using Dynamic logic and Transmission Gate

You made a static XOR gate in Lab3. In this lab, you will design two different XOR layouts using Schematic Editor as shown in Fig.L5.1. And after parameter extraction, you'll simulate the netlist using MySPICE. For simplicity, assume the complimentary signals are given as shown in Fig.L5.1. Make sure that the labels are, **A, B, AB, BB, CLK** and **Z**.

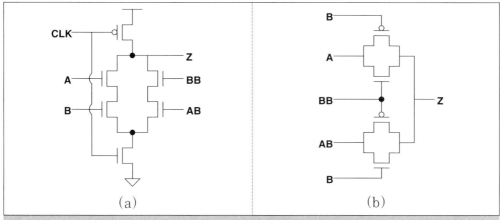

(a)   (b)

Fig.L5.1 XOR schematics: Dynamic vs. Transmission gate

In Fig.L5.1, the first XOR is implemented using the dynamic circuit
scheme while the other consists of two identical transmission gates.
The first one will be drawn as one level. Fig.L5.2 shows the stick
diagram for the dynamic circuit. The second XOR implementation will
be designed hierarchically using the transmission gate implemented in
Lab2. The procedures for drawing and simulating circuits are identical
to the previous labs. You can use the input deck of SPICE from Lab3.

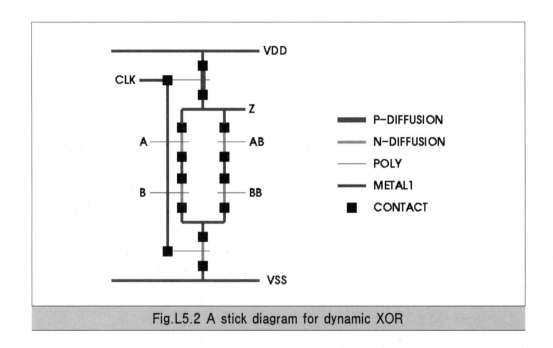

Fig.L5.2 A stick diagram for dynamic XOR

Question

Compare the given XOR gates with the XOR in Lab 3 on their size
and performance.

Chapter VII. Layout Considerations and Strategy for Design Changes

7.1 Considerations for IC Layout

7.1.1 Latch-up in Bulk CMOS

A byproduct of the Bulk CMOS structure is a pair of parasitic bipolar transistors. A phenomenon called latch-up is a very common problem in all CMOS processes, and special techniques have to be implemented in both circuit design and processing to minimize its impact. Fig.7.1 shows the cross-section and equivalent circuit of these four-layer devices. The collector of each BJT is connected to the base of the other transistor in a positive feedback structure. Latch-up can occur when (1) both BJT's conduct, creating a low resistance path between VDD and GND and (2) the product of the gains of the two transistors in the feedback loop, $\beta_1 \times \beta_2$, is greater than one. The result of latch-up is a circuit malfunction at the minimum, and results in the destruction of the device in the worst case.

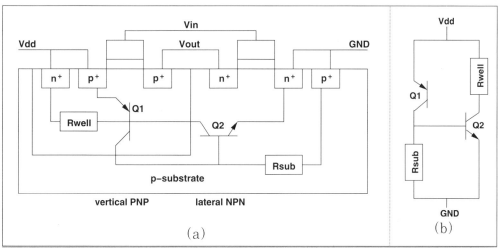

Fig.7.1(a) Cross section of parasitic transistors in Bulk CMOS and (b) Equivalent Circuit [WAE].

Latch-up may begin when Vout drops below GND due to a noise spike or an improper circuit hookup (Vout is the base of the lateral NPN Q2). If sufficient current flows through Rsub to turn on Q2 (I Rsub ⟩ 0.7 V), this will draw current through Rwell. If the voltage drop across Rwell is high enough, Q1 will also turn on, and a self-sustaining low resistance path between the power rails is formed. If the gains are such that $\beta_1 \times \beta_2 ⟩ 1$, latch-up may occur. Once latch-up has begun, the only way to stop it is to reduce the current below a critical level, usually by removing power from the circuit. The most likely place for latch-up to occur is in pad drivers, where large voltage transients and large currents are present.

Therefore, it is crucial to design the diffusion structures in I/O cells with great care. It is possible to construct a silicon-controlled rectifier (SCR) structure unwillingly, and instead of protecting the transistors, the SCR can enter a mode where it is latched on and conducting large enough currents to destroy the chip (latch-up). The source-substrate and drain-substrate diodes can become forward-biased due to power-supply bounce or output undershoot (the cell outputs fall below VSS) or overshoot (outputs rise greater than VDD). These injected minority carriers can travel fairly large distances and interact with nearby transistors causing latch-up. I/O cells normally surround the I/O transistors with guard rings (a continuous ring of n-diffusion in an n-well connected to VDD, and a ring of p-diffusion in a p-well connected to VSS) to collect these minority carriers. This is a problem that can also occur in the logic core and is one reason that substrate and well connections are normally included to the power supplies in every cell.

The following approaches can prevent the latch-up phenomenon:
  ⓐ Reduce the gain product $\beta_1 \times \beta_2$

- Move n-well and n+source/drain farther apart. This increases the width of the base of Q2 and reduces gain β_2 as well as circuit density .
- Buried n+ layer in well reduces gain of Q1.

❷ Reduce the well and substrate resistances, producing lower voltage drops
   - Higher substrate doping level reduces Rsub.
   - Reduce Rwell by making low resistance contact to GND
   - Guard rings around p- and/or n-well, with frequent contacts to the rings, reduces the parasitic resistances (See Fig.7.2).

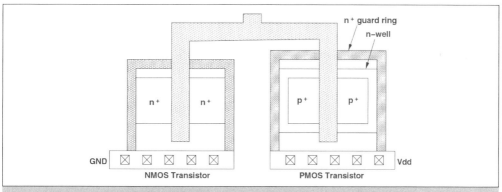

Fig.7.2 CMOS transistors with guard rings

❸ Make sure that the power supplies are off before plugging in a board. A "hot plug in" of an un-powered circuit board or module may cause signal pins to surge to voltages greater than 0.7V above VDD, which normally rises slower to its peak value. When the chip comes up to full power, sections of it could be latched.

❹ Carefully protect electrostatic devices associated with I/O pads with guard rings. Electrostatic discharge can trigger latch-up. ESD enters the circuit through an I/O pad, where it is clamped to one of the rails by the ESD protection circuit. Devices in the protection circuit can inject minority carriers in the substrate or well, potentially triggering latch-up.

ⓔ Radiation, including x-rays, cosmic, or alpha rays, can generate electron-hole pairs as they penetrate the chip. These carriers can contribute to well or substrate currents.

ⓕ Sudden transients on the power or ground bus, which may occur if large numbers of transistors switch simultaneously, can drive the circuit into latch-up. The possibility of this occurrence should be checked through simulation.

7.1.2 *Electromigration (EM)*

As semiconductor process engineering pushes towards providing increased circuit integration, circuit designers continue to take advantage of these gains by increasing circuit complexity and performance. To increase circuit performance, circuit currents often remain comparable despite the increased density. With the advent of the miniaturized integrated circuits, the current densities in the metal stripes on a chip can attain huge values (mA/cm^2). The usual way to obtain reliable circuits is to avoid such large current densities by having stripe widths of sufficiently large size. However, due to continuing miniaturization of very large scale integrated (VLSI) circuits, thin-film metallic conductors or interconnects are subject to increasingly high current densities. Under these conditions, EM can lead to the electrical failure of interconnects in relatively short times, reducing the circuit lifetime to an unacceptable level. Therefore, the EM problem remains of interest irrespective of the fact that more wire space is created by using many metal layers [YAC].

EM causes several different kinds of failure in narrow interconnect. The most familiar are void failures along the length of the line (called internal failures) and diffusive displacements at the terminals of the line that destroy electrical contact. The variation of all these microstructural parameters over a film causes a non-uniform distribution of atomic flow rate. Therefore non-zero atomic flux divergence exists at the places where the number of atoms flowing into the area is not equal to the number of atoms flowing out of that area per unit time. With the non-zero atomic flux divergence, there will be either a mass depletion (divergence > 0) or accumulation (divergence < 0), leading to formation of voids and hillocks. Then, failure results either from voids growing over the entire line width that cause breaking of the line or extrusions that cause short circuits to neighbouring lines. Next, the thermal accelerating process refers to the acceleration process of *EM* damage due to the local increase in temperature. And the increase of the local current density is referred as the current crowding effect. Since joule heating is proportional to the square of current density, the current crowding effect leads to a local temperature rise around the void that in turn further accelerates the void growth. The whole process continues till the void is large enough to break the line. Such a process can be seen in Fig.7.3.

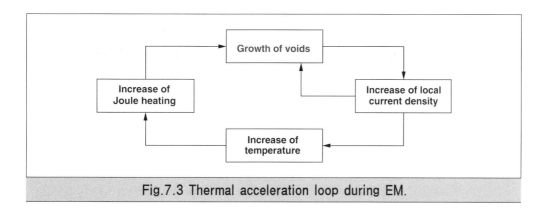

Fig.7.3 Thermal acceleration loop during EM.

Preventative measures must be taken against EM because this is an undetectable problem that develops in the field over time. EM can be computed using the RMS current based on: driver resistance, wire load, and gate load. Based on user-specified EM tolerance in the technology rules, the width should be sized just right and not too wide so that it doesn't waste routing space.

7.1.3 *The Crosstalk Problem in Deep Submicron Technology*

Noise, crosstalk and signal integrity have become critical problems in deep submicron technology. In older technologies, metal lines were wider and had much more spacing between them. As a result, the capacitance was primarily determined by area capacitance, or wire-to-substrate, which is dependent on the width of the wire and fringe or wire side-to-substrate capacitance, which is dependent on the height of the wire. Deep submicron technologies have thinner metal lines and have less space between adjacent wires as shown in Fig.7.4(b). Capacitance is primarily determined by sidewall capacitance, which is mainly constituted of wire-to-wire capacitance [RAB].

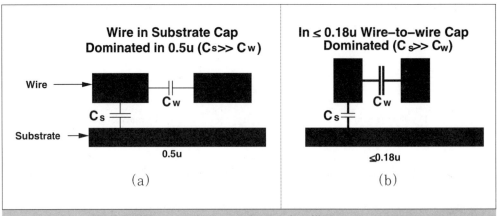

Fig.7.4 Wire to wire capacitance in silicon processes.

Spacing between wires determines wire-to-wire capacitance or coupling capacitance in deep submicron technologies. When spacing between wires is increased, coupling capacitance goes down. Noise effects are also reduced because noise directly correlates to coupling capacitance. Most high-end designers use extra spacing on critical nets to solve the coupling and crosstalk problems in the design. Fig.7.5 shows the coupling capacitance vs. wire spacing (the distance between wires). As shown in the figure, changing spacing from 0.6 micron to 1.0 micron, decreases coupling parasitics by 50%.

Signal shielding is a commonly used routing technique that prevents crosstalk and noise problems on sensitive nets by automatically adding grounded metal lines on each side of the chosen signal net. Differential pair routing recognizes that two adjacent lines are assumed to contain matched signal swings of opposite polarity.

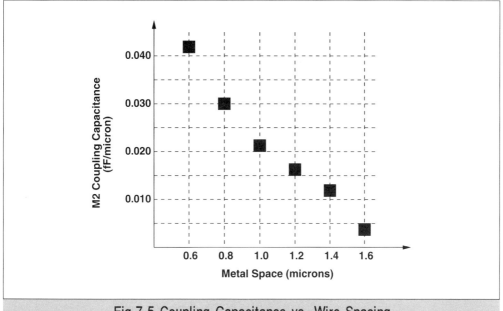

Fig.7.5 Coupling Capacitance vs. Wire Spacing

Signal integrity effects are becoming ever more visible for geometries of 0.18 micron and below. Routing complexity has increased dramatically and as a result more layers of metal are being added to silicon. To control the die size, the width of the metal is continuously being decreased whereas to keep the metal resistance low, the height of the metal wires is being increased. Furthermore, metal wire lengths are now longer than ever. For all these reasons, wires have now become longer and thinner and as a result the wire-to-wire capacitance between two conductors (Cw) has increased. Moreover, with more and more interconnect layers on a chip, the distance from the higher metal layers to the substrate layer increases, thereby decreasing the substrate capacitance component of the total net capacitance (Cs). Consequently, the wire-to-wire capacitance now dominates over the substrate capacitance in 0.18 micron and below. The overall result is an increased likelihood of signal corruption due to capacitive coupling between signals.

7.1.4 *Interconnect Delay in Deep Submicron Technology*

With silicon technologies of 0.18 micron widely available, the effect of interconnect delay on total path delay has become not just significant, but dominant. A typical timing path is shown in Fig.7.6.

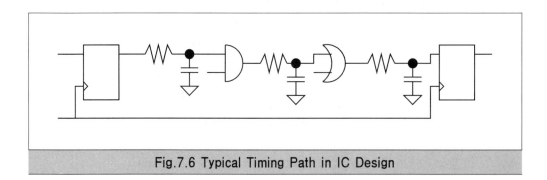

Fig.7.6 Typical Timing Path in IC Design

As the process shrinks, relative wire-to-wire capacitance increases. Older technologies have wider metal lines and capacitance is primarily determined by area capacitance and fringe capacitance. However, in deep sub micron technologies, metal lines are thinner and there is less space between adjacent wires. Therefore, the capacitance is primarily determined by sidewall capacitance or wire-to-wire capacitance, which is dependent on spacing between wires. Since interconnect delay is directly proportional to capacitance, same length wires will have longer delay in smaller geometry technologies in which wires are closer to each other. For example, a 5mm wire in 0.6 micron technology, which has an interconnect delay of 1ns, translates to 10 percent of a 100 MHz design and roughly 2-3x an average gate delay for that technology. The same wire in 0.18 micron technology will have a delay of 3ns, which translates to 70 percent of a 250 MHz design and a 30x average gate delay.

When using older silicon technology in which gate delays were dominant, the design methodology could focus on the design of the gates in the chip in order to optimize performance, and pay little attention to the interconnect part of the delay. In this traditional design methodology, the interconnect delays are estimated using the statistical wire load model. In 0.18 micron and below technologies, where the interconnect dominates the total delay, how the interconnect is modeled and how it is considered and routed during the design must be improved. Because the wires have the biggest effect within a delay path, design methodologies must be updated. More attention must be paid to the aspects of design that most affect interconnects.

7.1.5 *Inductive Effects*

Many VLSI components have multiple outputs. Serious problems can arise when many outputs switch simultaneously. This causes transient voltage drops in the inductances inherent in the ground and power interconnect, and in the bond wire and pins on the chip package. These effects are modeled in Fig.7.7.

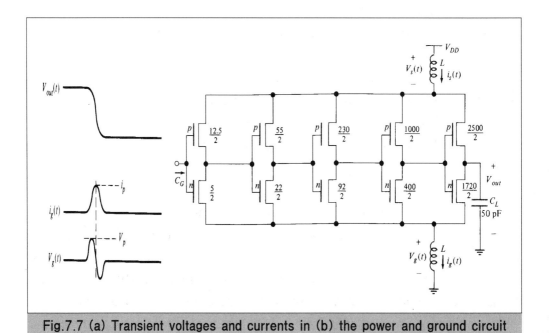

Fig.7.7 (a) Transient voltages and currents in (b) the power and ground circuit

Often the power and ground pins are located at the furthest corners of dual in-line packages. The inductance of the various power conductors lying between the I/O pad and the external pin ranges from 5 to 20 nH, depending on the specific dimensions. An output pad driver designed as outlined above will conduct large currents when switching typical off-chip loads (often up to 100 pF capacitance). For example, typical numbers for a single output driver are a rise or fall time of 5 ns with a peak current of 50 mA reached halfway through the switching time. With $L = 10$ nH, the peak value of the inductive voltage drop, $V_p(t)$ is

$$v_p(t) = L\frac{di}{dt} = 10nH * \frac{50mA}{2.5ns} = 0.2V$$

Although this on its own is not enough to cause problems, consider a design with 16 outputs. A bad situation would arise with one output low (and remaining low) while the other 15 outputs simultaneously switch from high to low. On the basis of the model described, the peak ground line voltage drop would be 15 * 0.2 = 3V. The output of the sixteenth driver (which was supposed to remain low) will thus be raised in potential by 3 Volts momentarily, producing a transient high logic level, quite possibly introducing a logic error. A corresponding effect arises in the VDD conductor. Such errors can be reduced by:

ⓐ Using the lowest inductance pins for power and ground
ⓑ Using additional parallel pins for power and ground
ⓒ Reducing off-chip capacitive loads
ⓓ Designing output pad drivers with deliberately slower rise and fall times.

7.1.6 Decoupling Capacitance

On the rising/falling edge of the clock all the flip flops on the die may be clocked within a nanosecond or so of each other, resulting in large current flows through the ground and power pins. The current surge is mainly due to the capacitance driven by the clock and by flip-flops changing their state on the clock. The connections from the ground and power pins to the die have inductance, as do the connections within the die. The ground and power on the die will bounce up and down at the clock frequency and this will be coupled to all the other I/O lines that are clamped to power or ground by transistors. To minimize this bouncing, a low impedance path from the pairs of ground and power pins to decoupling capacitors should be provided as shown in Fig.7.8.

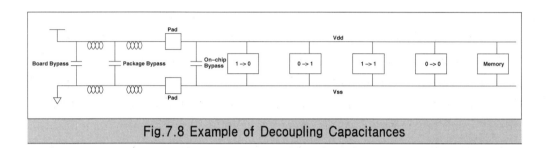

Fig.7.8 Example of Decoupling Capacitances

A low inductance connection is obtained by a short and wide trace leading to the feedthrough to the ground plane. A pair of feedthroughs has less inductance than a single feedthrough. The power pins should be connected by a low inductance path to the power plane, or if there is no power plane, to a decoupling capacitor.

7.1.7 ESD Protection

The gate oxide in CMOS transistors is extremely thin (100 Å or less). This leaves the gate oxide of the I/O cell input transistors susceptible to breakdown from static electricity (electrostatic discharge, or ESD). ESD arises when human or machines handle the package leads. Sometimes this problem is called electrical overstress (EOS) since most ESD-related failures are caused not by gate-oxide breakdown, but by the thermal stress (melting). This occurs when the n-channel transistor in an output driver overheats (melts) due to the large current flow in the drain diffusion connected to a pad during an ESD event.

To protect the I/O cells from ESD, the input pads are normally tied to device structures that clamp the input voltage to below the gate breakdown voltage (which can be as low as 10 V with a 100 Å gate oxide). Some I/O cells use transistors with a special ESD implant that increases breakdown voltage and provides protection. I/O driver transistors can also use elongated drain structures (ladder structures) and large drain-to-gate spacing to help limit current, but in a salicide process that lowers the drain resistance this is difficult. One solution is to mask the I/O cells during the salicide step. Another solution is to use PNPN and NPNP diffusion structures called silicon-controlled rectifiers (SCRs) to clamp voltages and divert current to protect the I/O circuits from ESD.

There are several ways to model the capability of an I/O cell to withstand EOS. The human-body model (HBM) represents ESD by a 100 pF capacitor discharging through a 1.5 kΩ resistor (this is an International Electro-technical Committee, IEC, specification). Typical voltages generated by the human body are in the range of 2-4 kV, and we often see an I/O pad cell rated by the voltage it can withstand using the HBM. The machine model represents an ESD event generated by automated machine handlers. Typical machine model parameters use a 200 pF capacitor (typically charged to 200 V) discharged through a 25 Ω resistor, corresponding to a peak initial current of nearly 10 A. The charge-device model (also called device charge-discharge) represents the problem when an IC package is charged, in a shipping tube for example, and then grounded. If the maximum charge on a package is 3nC and the package capacitance to

CMOS VLSI Layout Artwork Design and Lab ·······································

ground is 1.5 pF, it is simulated by charging a 1.5 pF capacitor to 2 kV and discharging it through a 1 Ω resistor.

7.2 **Strategy for Design Changes**

7.2.1 *Engineering Change Order*

Current VLSI chip design involves very complex and large circuits for which various metrics like power, speed and area need to be optimized, and various technological effects like noise, crosstalk and thermal distribution need to be addressed. These complexities will further increase in future chip designs. Often after a chip layout is completed, simulation can reveal problems with one or more of the optimization metrics and/or technological constraints. In such cases, design engineers resort to re-synthesizing small portions of the circuit in order to correct the problem---this is the so-called engineering change order (ECO) process. Typically after such re-synthesis, which can include logic re-synthesis of some functions (e.g., factoring, gate duplication), cell re-synthesis (e.g., gate re-sizing), buffer insertion, etc., a small portion of the circuit netlist is changed. In order to capitalize on the enormous resources and time already spent on the physical design of the chip and to meet time-to-market requirements, it is desirable to re-layout only the affected portion of the circuit, while minimizingany layout changes of the much larger unaffected part of the circuit. Further, independent of other re-synthesis, a physical re-design of small portions of the circuit may also be needed to better optimize the objectives(s) of interest and/or to satisfy technological constraints (e.g., some cells and nets on critical paths may need to be re-placed and re-routed in order to meet speed requirements).

Therefore, routers for high-performance designs have to be predictable. The router should take the same or similar path when only small changes are made to the design. This helps the designer predict the interconnect delays throughout the design cycle. It is also becoming increasingly important to support incremental changes in layout through an engineering change order (ECO) capability. Since ECOs are done at a very late stage in the design cycle, the router should only minimally disturb existing nets when implementing any ECOs. This guarantees a faster timing convergence and avoids late stage surprises for long interconnect delays.

If the algorithms to estimate congestion in the floorplanning tool accurately, and perfectly reflect the algorithms used by the global router and detailed router, routing completion should be guaranteed. Often, however, the detailed router will not be able to completely route all the nets. These problematical nets are known as unroutes. Routers handle this situation in one of two ways. The first method leaves the problematical nets unconnected. The second method completes all interconnects anyway but with some design-rule violations (the problematical nets may be shorted to other nets, for example). Some tools flag these problems as a warning (in fact there can be no more serious error).

If there are many un-routings, the designer needs to discover the reason and return to the floorplanner and change channel sizes (for a cell-based ASIC) or increase the base-array size (for a gate array). Returning to the global router and changing bin sizes or adjusting the algorithms may also help. In drastic cases, it may be necessary to change the floorplan. If just a handful of difficult nets remain to be routed, some tools allow the designer to perform hand edits using a rip-up and reroute router (sometimes this is done automatically by the detailed router as a last phase in the routing procedure anyway).

All of this places a paramount importance on the development of efficient algorithms to perform incremental physical design (layout re-synthesis); to date only a few methods have been developed in these areas. Placement and routing are two major components of physical design, and in this project efficient algorithms will be developed to perform these tasks incrementally. These incremental placement and routing algorithms will have the following goals: (1) To be orders of magnitude faster than complete placement and routing; (2) To tackle optimization of speed and/or power, and satisfaction of technological constraints in problematic parts of the circuit; For the incremental routing algorithm, additional goals are: (3) To complete the required incremental routing in the available channel area if such a solution exists (this will minimize resorting to area-and time-expensive expansion of routing channels); (4) To complete the routing without significantly changing electrical properties (e.g., power, delay) of existing nets (this will keep the parasitic extraction data and timing/power analysis for the unaffected portion of the circuit valid).

7.2.2 Space Logic and Spare Lines

Even if the most advanced tools and experts are used, a chip will always have some dead space central enough to make the idea of spare logic gates and spare lines worthwhile. Unless the chip has a flat netlist and the design team is using an automated place-and-route tool, any design will end up with holes of unused area. After expending the effort needed to implement last-minute changes and after feeling the pain of bug fixes and mask revisions to revise only a small portion of a design, many designers have accepted the idea of placing unused or spare gates and signals on the chip before tape-out.

A simple technique is to devise a block of logic that compromises a common group of logical functions and place the cell in any free area in the chip design. The quantity and types of gates that are used may vary from chip to chip based on a forecast of what may fail. The design of the block is heavily metal oriented so that connections and reconfiguration of the transistors are easily done using a minimum number of layers. The gates are disabled initially in such a way that they do not affect the normal operation of the chip. Combined with spare lines that connect various regions of the chip and passing by the groups of spare logic, fixes to minor bugs become much easier. Additionally, lines are not a great impact on chip size when compared to missing a market window.

Spare lines are routed in every channel, and in general up to 5 percent of the number of signals in the channel should be spares, not including routing requirements for the chip's finishing stage. During the prototyping stage, it is a good practice to have at least two spare lines per channel. The spare lines respect channel metal directions and are fully connected from one end of the chip to another. Using numerous local spare structures, global changes can be implemented without any chip impact on thesize or schedule impact.

CMOS VLSI Layout Artwork Design and Lab ··································

References

[YAC] Young, D., and A. Christou, " Failure mechanism models for electromigration." *IEEE Transactions on Reliability*, Vol. 43, no. 2, pp. 186-192, 1994.

[WAE] N.H.E. Weste and K. Eshraghian, *Principles of CMOS VLSI Design*, Addison-Wesley Publishing Company, Second Edition, 1993.

[RAB] J.M. Rabaey, *Digital Integrated Circuits*, Prentice Hall, 1996.

LAB6. Logic Simulation (State Machine)

In this lab we will examine the most important kind of sequential circuit: the finite state machine. *Finite state machines* are so named because the sequential logic that implements them can be in only a fixed number of possible states. More generally, the outputs and next state of a finite state machine are combinational logic functions of the inputs and present state. The choice of next state can depend on the value of an input, leading to more complex behavior than that of counters. Finite state machines are critical for realizing the control and decision-making logic in digital-systems.

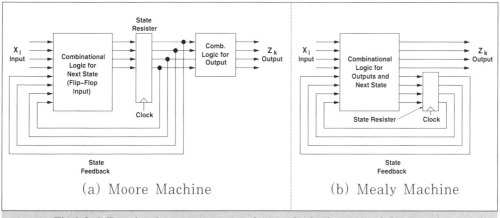

(a) Moore Machine   (b) Mealy Machine

Fig.L6.1 Two basic ways to organize a clocked sequential network.

Both Moore and Mealy finite state machines consist of flip-flops whose inputs are logical combinations of the input signals and the values of the flip-flop outputs. They differ in how the outputs of the machine are determined. For a Moore machine the outputs depend *only* on the flip-flop outputs. For a Mealy machine the outputs depend on both the flip-flop outputs and the current inputs. Thus the outputs of a Mealy machine can change whenever the inputs change, even if this occurs "between clock pulses". In the figure, we see that the output of a Moore machine is associated with the state itself, whereas with a Mealy machine the output is associated with both the state the machine is now in and the current values of the inputs.

In general if a machine has N states, it will require M flip-flops, where M is the smallest number such that N is less than or equal to 2^M. If the system has D inputs, there are 2^D paths flowing out of each state. If there are K outputs, for a Moore machine each state is labeled with K output values; for a Mealy machine each path is labeled with K outputs.

In this lab, we shall learn methods for describing the behavior of finite state machines. The most difficult problem the novice hardware designer faces is mapping an imprecise behavioral specification of an FSM into a more precise description, for example, a state diagram, state tables, a schematic, or a VHDL program. In this section we will illustrate the process by examining several detailed case studies: an FSM that can recognize patterns in its inputs using MyLogic Schematic Editor, MyVHDL, and Logic Simulator.

Pre-Lab: A Finite String Recognizer

Finite state machines are often used to recognize patterns in an input sequence. Consider the following finite state machine specification: "A finite state recognizer has one input and one output. The output is asserted whenever the input sequence 0, 1, 0 has been observed."

The following Moore type state machine detects the sequence $F_3 = 0, 1, 0$. Start by filling in a string of states, assuming that the sequence is immediately received. The legend shows that the state name of each bubble is drawn above the output, which is named *detect*. The state name *Mm* indicates that following a RESET, to arrive at the given state, the Greatest common Prefix-Suffix Subsequence (GPSS) must have a length of m bits. You can also think of m as representing the current number of *potential* matches between the received sequence and flag sequence. The descriptive phrases above the bubbles indicate that after a RESET no matches are made, and that until a detection is made only *potential* matches exist between the received sequence and flag sequence.

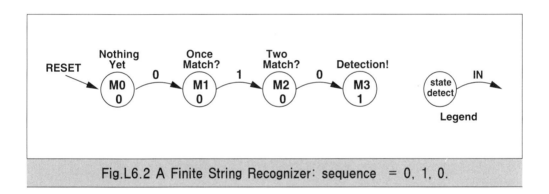

Fig.L6.2 A Finite String Recognizer: sequence = 0, 1, 0.

Almost half of the job is done already. To fill in the rest of the state diagram, remember that a one bit input causes each state to lead to two possible next states. Consider *M0*: Suppose that following a RESET, a '1' is received rather than a '0'. What will the next state be? Given $R_1 = 1$ and $F_3 = 0,1,0$, GPSS is NULL (m=0) so that the next state is *M0*. Another way to think of this is that 1 simply does not match the first bit in the flag sequence.

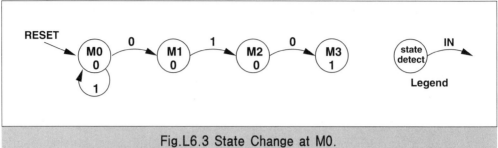

Fig.L6.3 State Change at M0.

Next, following a reset suppose that $R_2 = 0,0$ is received, what will the final state be? We know that the first bit in R_2 brings us to *M1*, but what state follows *M1*? We find that GPSS is 0 (m=1) so the final state is M1. Another way to think of this is that only the new bit 0 serves as a potential match with the flag sequence.

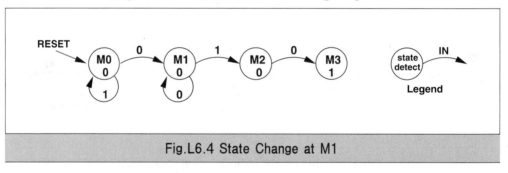

Fig.L6.4 State Change at M1

Following a reset suppose that $R_3 = 0$, 1, 1, what will the final state be? GPSS is NULL (m=0) so the last state is *M0*.

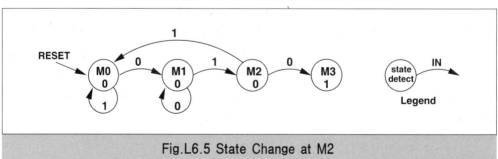

Fig.L6.5 State Change at M2

Following a reset suppose that R_4 = 0, 1, 0, 0, what will the state be after detection? GPSS is 0 (m=1) so *M1*. Conversely if R_4 = 0, 1, 0, 1, we find that GPSS is 0, 1 (m=2) so that the final state is *M2*. The preceding discussion leads to the following state diagram.

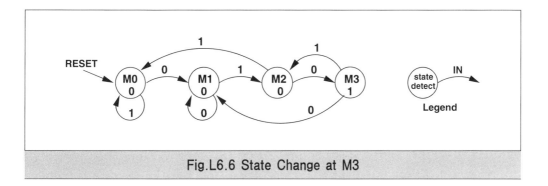

Fig.L6.6 State Change at M3

Procedure 1: Design of Mealy State Machine

Problem

Design a Mealy finite State Machine that accepts an input binary sequence such as 001010011101.... Its output is zero except when the number of 1's that have been input is a multiple of three. Implement the machine using as few flip-flops as possible, and using only D-flip-flops. In the example below, the output that is observed after each input bit is received is shown directly below the input bit received:

input (X): 1 0 1 1 0 1 1 1 0 1 1 0 1 1 0...
output(Z): 0 0 0 1 0 0 1 0 0 0 0 0 0 1 0...

Solution : Finite State Machine Design Procedure

Step 1 : *Understand the problem.* A finite state machine is often described in terms of an English-language specification of its behavior. It is important that you interpret this description in an unambiguous manner. For counters, it is sufficient simply to enumerate the sequence. For finite state machines, try some input sequences to be sure you understand the conditions under which the various outputs are generated. Find the states for this machine.

Step 2 : *Determine how many flip flops are required.* For a machine with three states, count up to the next power of 2, which is 4, which is 2 raised to the second power, so two flip-flops are needed.

Step 3 : *Obtain an abstract representation of the FSM.* Once you understand the problem, you must place it in a form that is easy to manipulate by the procedures for implementing the finite state machine. A state diagram is one possibility. Other representations, to be introduced in the next solution, include algorithmic state machines and specifications in hardware description languages.

Step 4 : *Choose flip-flop types for implementing the FSM's state.* This is identical to the decision in the counter design procedure. *J-K* flip-flops tend to reduce gate count at the expense of more connections. *D* flip-flops simplify the implementation process. Write down the state transition table, which lists for every possible state and input combination what the next state will be, and what the current output is.

Step 5 : *Perform state minimization.* Step 2, deriving the abstract representation, often results in a description that has too many states. Certain paths through the state machine can be eliminated because their input/output behavior is duplicated by other functionally equivalent paths. This is a new step, not needed in the simpler detector design process. Set up a Karnaugh map for each flip-flop input, and for each output. Find the minimal combinational circuit that accurately represents each quantity.

Step 6 : *Implement the finite state machine.* The final step is also found in the detector design procedure. Using Boolean equations or K-maps for the next state and output combinational functions, produce the minimized two-level or multilevel implementation. Draw the circuit.

Step 7 : *Simulate the code using MyLogic Simulator.*

Questions

❶ Suppose you are told that a Mealy machine is implemented with three flip-flops, two inputs, and six asynchronous outputs. Consider the *complete* state diagram for this machine (that is, there are no don't cares). Answer the following questions:

What are the minimum and maximum number of states in the state diagram?

What are the minimum and maximum number of transition arrows starting at a particular state?

What are the minimum and maximum number of transition arrows that can end in a particular state?

What are the minimum and maximum number of different binary patterns that can be displayed on the outputs?

❷ Suppose you are told that a Moore machine has five flip-flops, three inputs, and nine outputs. Answer the following questions:

What are the minimum and maximum number of states in the state diagram?

What are the minimum and maximum number of transition arrows starting at a particular state?

What are the minimum and maximum number of transition arrows that can end in a particular state?

What are the minimum and maximum number of different binary patterns that can be displayed on the outputs?

❸ Derive the state transition table for the schematic implementation of the finite state machine of the following figure (the next-state and output functions are implemented by a PLA structure). The machine has one input I and one output Z.

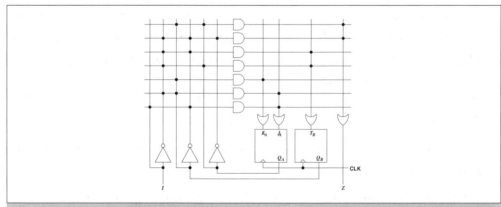

Fig.L6.7 A finite state machine schematic

Chapter VIII. Full Chip Layout and Issues

Traditionally the layout process of integrated circuits is divided into several phases. The most common way of breaking up the layout problem is first to do component placement, and then to determine the approximate course for connecting the wires in a global-routing phase. This phase may be followed by a topological compaction, after which a detailed-routing phase determines the exact course of the wires. A geometric-compaction phase may further reduce the area requirement of the layout.

8.1 Partitioning

In partitioning a system, each logic cell needs to be weighted according to its area in order to control the total areas of each IC. This can be done if the area of each logic cell can either be calculated or estimated. There will be many objectives or constraints that should be taken into account during partitioning. For example, certain logic cells in a system may need to be located on the same IC in order to avoid adding the delay of any external interconnections. Or, some logic cells may consume more power than others and you may need to add power constraints to avoid exceeding the power-handling capability of a single ASIC.

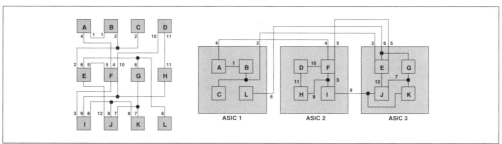

Fig.8.1 Partitioning example. (a) a system. (b) A partitioning with five external connections (nets 2, 4, 5, 6, and 8) (requirement: the network into three ICs with no more than four logic cells per IC) [MJS].

Fig.8.1(a) shows a simple network [GOT]. There are 12 logic cells, labeled A-L, connected by 12 nets (labeled 1-12). At this level, each logic cell is a large circuit block which might be RAM, ROM, an ALU, and so on. Each net might also be a bus, but, for the moment, we'll assume that each net is a single connection and all nets are weighted equally. Fig.8.1(b) shows a partitioning with five external connections: two of the ICs have three pins; the third has four pins.

8.2 Chip Floorplanning

8.2.1 *Aspect Ratio*

The objectives of floorplanning are to minimize the chip area and minimize delay. Each of the RTL blocks and the pre-designed IP cores (RAM, CPU, etc.) are arranged on the die. The size and timing of the cores is known, but the designer must estimate the timing and area of the RTL blocks. The designer uses previous experience to estimate the block size and timing to create black boxes. This initial floorplan is the input to the first routing phase. Later, when the actual RTL code is written for each block, the user-estimated black box models are replaced with gate-level netlists generated by synthesis tools. Synthesis constraints, such as budgets for intra-block delay and block I/O boundary conditions, should also be considered. The netlist itself may need to be modified through driver sizing, repeater insertion and buffer clustering. Block layout is paramount, as well as performance-driven routing directives for block layout, such as wire tapering, spacing, shielding, etc. Thus, route planning entails the modeling of hierarchical and area pins and understanding power/area/delay tradeoffs in both devices and interconnects.

It is necessary to control the **aspect ratio** of our floorplan because we have to fit our chip into the **die cavity** (a fixed-size hole, usually square) inside a package. Fig.8.2(a)-(c) show how we can rearrange our chip to achieve a square aspect ratio. Fig.8.2(c) also shows a **congestion map**. Shading indicates the ratio of channel density to the channel capacity. Dark areas show regions that cannot be routed because the channel congestion exceeds the estimated capacity. In Fig.8.2(d), resizing flexible blocks A and C alleviates congestion.

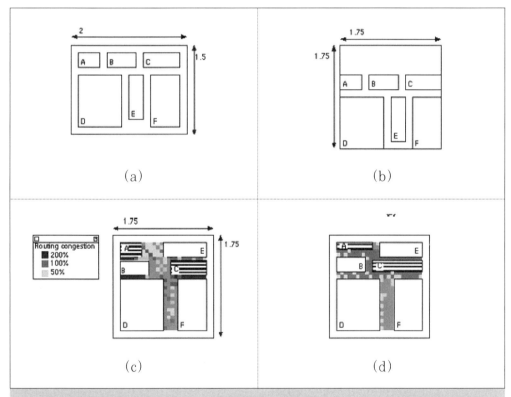

Fig.8.2 Congestion analysis. (a) The initial floorplan with a 2:1.5 die aspect ratio. (b) Altering the floorplan to give a 1:1 chip aspect ratio. (c) A trial floorplan with a congestion map. Blocks A and C have been placed so that we know the terminal positions in the channels. (d) Resizing flexible blocks A and C alleviates congestion [MJS].

8.2.2 I/O and Power Planning

One consideration in pad placement is that the pads should be near the perimeter of the chip. The bonding machine may spatter metal and do damage to the circuitry if it has to reach into the center. Some fabrication processes even require that no active circuitry be placed outside of the pads. Others, however, allow pads anywhere on the chip. Another reason to place pads on the edge is to keep the bonding wires from crossing. The pads must present an uncluttered view from the outside of the chip.

In addition to being located on the edge of the chip, pads should also be placed uniformly. This means that there must be approximately the same number of pads on all four edges and that they must be spaced evenly along each edge. On special chips that have rectangular layout, the pads must be evenly spaced along only two edges. Equal spacing makes automatic bonding easier, and uniform pad density keeps the bonding wires from cluttering and possibly shorting. The proper limitations of pad spacing must also be taken into consideration.

Every chip communicates with the outside world. Signals flow onto and off the chip and we need to supply power. It is also necessary to consider the I/O and power constraints early in the floorplanning process. Fig.8.3(a) shows a pad-limited die and Fig.8.3(b) shows a core-limited die. On a pad-limited die we use tall, thin pad-limited pads, which maximize the number of pads we can fit around the outside of the chip. On a core-limited die we use short, wide core-limited pads. Fig.8.3(c) shows how we can use both types of pads to change the aspect ratio of a die to be different from that of the core.

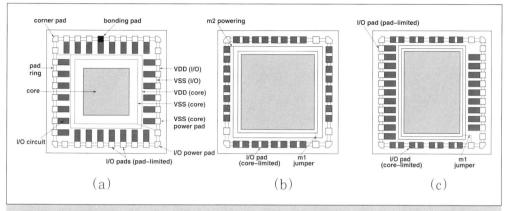

Fig.8.3 Pad-limited and core-limited die. (a) A pad-limited die. The number of pads determines the die size. (b) A core-limited die: The core logic determines the die size. (c) Using both pad-limited pads and core-limited pads for a square die [MJS].

Another concern in proper pad layout is the location of power and ground pads. Power pads are used for the positive supply, or VDD, power buses and the ground or negative supply, VSS or GND. Usually one set of VDD/VSS pads supplies one power ring that runs around the pad ring and supplies power to the I/O pads only. Another set of VDD/VSS pads connects to a second power ring that supplies the logic core. I/O pads also contain special circuits to protect against electrostatic discharge (ESD). These circuits can withstand very short high-voltage (several kilovolt) pulses that can be generated during human or machine handling.

Fig.8.4 shows one configuration of power, ground, and pads. The ground runs outside of the pads because it is less critical than the power rail, which runs just inside. This arrangement allows each pad to have easy access to the supply voltages it needs to function properly. In order to get these voltages to the chip, however, there must be a gap in the inner power rail. Although it is possible to introduce over-voltages onto the chip via the supply connections, it is not feasible to provide any form of protection on these lines. They are, in any case, less sensitive to over-voltage than the signal connection. There is an advantage to using multiple power supply pads if the area is available, because this reduces noise levels. The necessary bus width must be calculated from the power requirements of the chip circuitry to:

- Keep the voltage drops within acceptable limits.
- Keep the current density below the level that causes electro-migration in the aluminum.

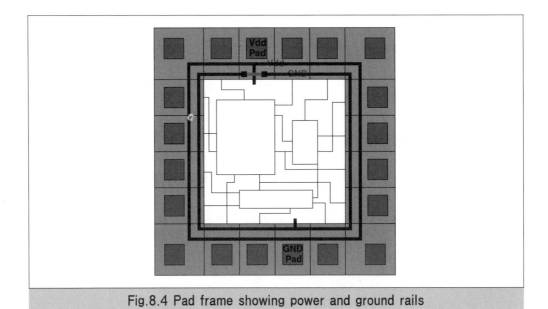

Fig.8.4 Pad frame showing power and ground rails

8.3 Placement

During the floorplanning step, the areas between blocks are assigned for interconnect. Placement is the process of positioning cells such that they connect well and do not waste space. After completing a floorplan, placement of the logic cells within the flexible blocks can be started. The goal of a placement tool is to arrange all the logic cells within the flexible blocks on a chip.

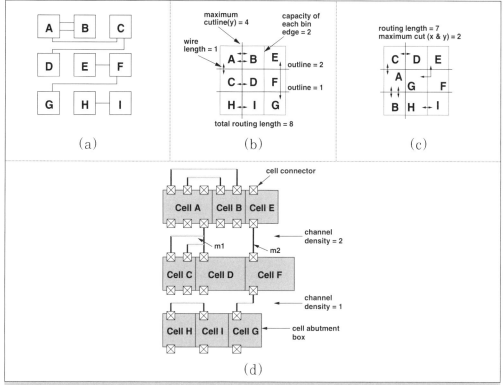

Fig.8.5 Placement example. (a) An example network. (b) In this placement, the bin size is equal to the logic cell size and all the logic cells are assumed equal size. (c) An alternative placement with a lower total routing length. (d) A layout that might result from the placement shown in b [MJS].

Fig.8.5 shows an example network and placements to illustrate the measures for interconnect length and interconnect congestion. Fig.8.5(b) and (c) illustrate the meaning of total routing length, the maximum cut line in the x-direction, the maximum cut line in the y-direction, and the maximum density. In this example, it is assumed that the logic cells are all the same size, connections can be made to terminals on any side, and the routing channels between each adjacent logic cell have a capacity of 2. Fig.8.5(d) shows what the completed layout might look like.

8.4 Routing a Design

Routing usually involves two steps, global routing and detailed routing. Global routing creates a path for every interconnect, even though this path is not yet physically exact. Detailed routing then follows, which determines the width and spacing needed for each different metal layer. A route may connect multiple metal layers and use vias to switch from one metal layer to another. After detailed routing, a Design Rule Checker (DRC) ensures that detailed routes meet all of the manufacturing requirements, such as not permitting short circuits between wires, adherence to metal width and spacing rules, and accommodating via rules. Designers also check that the interconnects meet all the timing budgets and eliminate any crosstalk, noise or signal integrity problems. The goal of global routing is to provide complete instructions to the detailed router on where to route every net.

Fig.8.6 shows an example of global routing for a net with five terminals, labeled A1 through F1. If a designer wishes to use minimum total interconnect path length as an objective, the global router finds the minimum-length tree shown in Fig.8.6(b). This tree determines the channels the interconnects will use. For example, the shortest connection from A1 to B1 uses channels 2, 1, and 5 (in that order). This is the information the global router passes to the detailed router. Fig.8.6(c) shows that minimizing the total path length may not correspond to minimizing the path delay between two points.

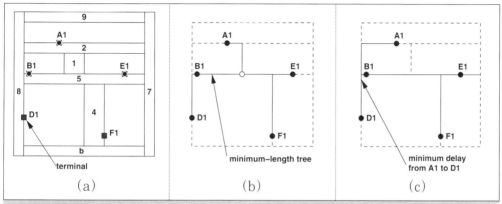

(a)   (b)   (c)

Fig.8.6 (a) A cell-based ASIC showing a single net with a fanout of four (five terminals). (b) The terminals are projected to the center of the nearest channel, forming a graph. (c) The minimum-length tree does not necessarily correspond to minimum delay [MJS].

The goal of detailed routing is to complete all the connections between logic cells. The most common objective is to minimize one or more of the following:

- The total interconnect length and area.
- The number of layer changes that the connections have to make.
- The delay of critical paths.
- Minimizing the number of layer changes corresponds to minimizing the number of vias that add parasitic resistance and capacitance to a connection.

The global routing step determines the channels to be used for each interconnect. Using this information, the exact location and layers for each interconnect are determined at the detailed routing stage.

Fig.8.7(a) depicts a two-level metal version showing the space between rows or slices of the datapath. In this case there are many connections to be brought out to the right of the datapath, and this causes the routing channel to be larger than normal and thus easily seen. Fig.8.7(b) shows a three-level metal version of the same datapath. In this case, more of the routing is completed over the top of the datapath slices, reducing the size of the routing channel.

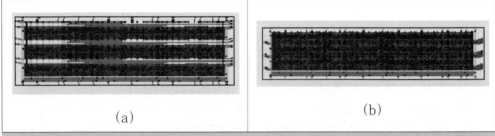

(a)　　　　　　　　　　　　　　　　(b)

Fig.8.7 Results of routing a datapath. (a) Implemented in a two-level metal process. (b) Implemented in a three-level metal process.

8.5 Full Chip Verification Process

Electro-migration width, for example, 1mA/mm, should be used to size power buses based on the power estimates supplied by designer of each block. The physical design should be implemented as immune as possible to analog/digital cross talk. This can be accomplished by separating the analog and digital power domains. The macro-blocks may be placed and routed several times during the floorplanning phase of the project to fine-tune the chip-level area estimation and aspect ratio of the blocks. Placement and routing is done strictly to minimize wire lengths and reduce congestion, rather than a timing driven method. The analog signals should be shielded from the digital part which makes a severe noise resulting in mal-function of the analog part.

During top level routing the channels between the top-level blocks may not be allowed to compact. This results in a slightly larger die size, but will allow hand manipulation of critical analog signals as well as changes to the top level without re-routing the entire IC. It is important to avoid re-verification of all signals if ECOs are required. The majority of the effort on the top-level Chip Assembly is the pre-routing of power and ground.

The layout is verified for any physical placements that violate the process fabrication rules which can cause the design to function improperly. The Design Rule Checker (DRC) verifies technology dependent physical design rules like minimum metal widths and spacing. This check is run on the entire IC including the pad frame. An Electrical Rule Check (ERC) looks for simple problems, such as open nodes and transistor shorts. This check must be re-run after any changes to the database prior to tape-out, and any violations must be fixed or waived by the foundry.

The final layout will then be compared with the mapped gate-level schematic from the front-end process by using Layout Versus Schematic (LVS) to verify that the layout is indeed a faithful representation of the mapped design. After verification, the layout is taped out for the mask pattern generation process in preparation for fabrication. This check must be re-run after any changes to the database prior to tape-out, and any violations must be fixed or waived by the designers.

Next, a Layout Parasitic Extraction (LPE) of the entire digital section of the IC is done. The output of this is a file with net-names and associated capacitance for inclusion in back-annotated simulation. The extraction data is important for design accuracy. This file will be used for post layout simulation.

Designers can provide their design in a data format, GDSII. Final preparation for the mask layout includes alignment marks, mask identification and other artifacts required in fabrication, the scribe lines and any special edge-seal structures. The design is then transformed and generated into various mask layers by Boolean Operations, sizing, inversion, coordinate transformations and scaling before being transferred to the mask shop for mask making.

References

[GOT] S. Goto, and T. Matsud, "Partitioning, assignment and placement." In *Layout Design and Verification*. Vol. 4 of *Advances in CAD for VLSI* (T. Ohtsuki, Ed.) pp. 55-97, 1986.

[MJS] Michael John Sebastian and John Smith, Application-Specific Integrated Circuits, Wesley Publishing Company, 1997.

LAB7. Measuring Parameters

Using MyAnalog Schematic Editor, MySPICE and Mypostprocessor, find the following parameters for both a P and an N type transistor:

Threshold Voltage: The gate-source voltage at which a transistor starts to conduct.

Saturation Velocity: Maximum velocity which can be obtained in a specific semiconductor

Body Effect: The variation of the threshold voltage of an FET due to a variation of the substrate or bulk voltage.

Channel length modulation: Variation of the channel due to an increase of the depletion region when increasing the drain voltage. A reduction of the channel yields a higher current.

Step 1 Measuring Threshold Voltages

Using MyAnalog Schematic Editor, create a circuit as shown in Fig.L7.1. Plot the Ids (Y axis) vs. Vgs (x axis) of a transistor (W = 10 μm, L = 10μm). Connect the drain of the transistor to a 0.1volt supply. Let Vgs vary from 0 to 2 volts. In the linear region, $I_d = k [(V_{gs} - V_t) V_{ds} - 0.5 V_{ds}^2]$, where $k = \mu\varepsilon_{ox} / T_{ox} (W/L)$. The slope of the straight line of the plot will intersect the X axis, when $I_d = 0$, thus $V_t = V_{gs} - 0.5 V_{ds}$. Note that VthN (the threshold voltage of the N type transistor) and VthP (the threshold voltage of the P type transistor) are in the linear region. Use AD = AS = 100p, and PD = PS = 30μ. These restrictions apply to all of the steps in this lab.

VthN = _____ V   VthP = _____ V

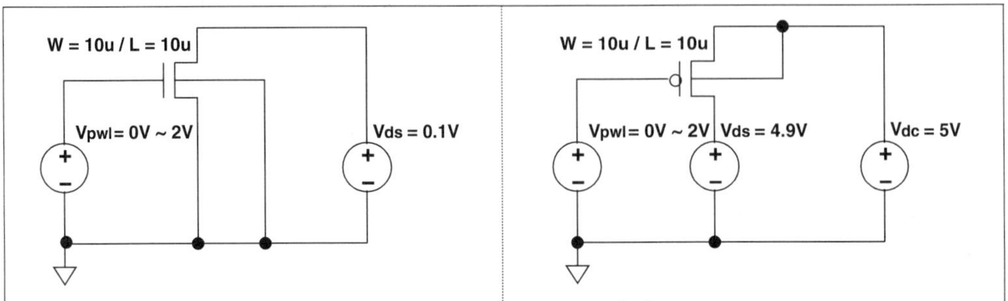

W = 10u / L = 10u

Vpwl= 0V ~ 2V   Vds = 0.1V

+
−   +
                      −

(a) Measuring VthN

W = 10u / L = 10u

Vpwl= 0V ~ 2V   Vds = 4.9V   Vdc = 5V

+   +   +
−   −   −

(b) Measuring VthP

Fig.L7.1 Setup for measuring threshold voltages.

Step 2 Measuring Saturation Gains

KpN Sat (the saturated gain of the N type transistor) and KpP Sat (the saturated gain of the P type transistor) – Plot the [sqrt(Ids)] (Y axis) vs. Vgs (X axis) of a transistor to a 5 volt supply. Let Vgs vary from 0 to 2 volts. The slope of the straight line will be equal to sqrt[(Kps/2)(W/L)]. For this case, you can assume that Weff/Leff = 1.

KpN Sat = _____ $\mu A/V^2$ KpP Sat = _____ $\mu A/V^2$

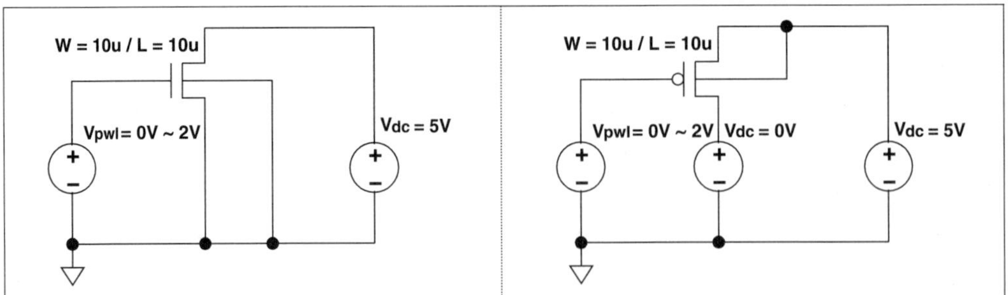

W = 10u / L = 10u

Vpwl= 0V ~ 2V   Vdc = 5V

+   +
−   −

(a) Measuring Kpn (SAT)

W = 10u / L = 10u

Vpwl= 0V ~ 2V   Vdc = 0V   Vdc = 5V

+   +   +
−   −   −

(b) Measuring Kpp (SAT)

Fig.L7.2 Setup for measuring saturation gains.

182

Step 3 Measuring Back Body Effects

γN(gamma, N channel back body effect-long channel) and γP (gamma, P channel back body effect-long channel).

Make multiple plots of the [sqrt(Ids)] (Y axis) vs. Vgs (X axis) of a transistor (W=10 μm, L=10 μm) with the gate connected to the Vgs power supply. Connect the drain to a fixed voltage of 0.1 volt. Tie the body to a negative power supply, Vbs. Let Vgs vary from 0 to 2 volts. Use values of Vbs of 0, 2, and 5 volts. Find the threshold voltage of the transistor at the three different values of Vbs. Assume that Ø0 = 0.7 volts. Find the value of r with Vbs of 0 to 2 volts and 0 to 5 volts using the following equation: $\triangle$Vth= γ[(Vsb+Ø0)^0.5 -(Ø0)^0.5]. Also find the average value of γ for the three measurements.

VthN (0 v)	= _____ V	VthP (0)	= _____ V
VthN (2 v)	= _____ V	VthP (2)	= _____ V
VthN (5 v)	= _____ V	VthP (5)	= _____ V
$\triangle$VthN (0 - 2 v) = _____ V		$\triangle$VthP (0 - 2v) = _____ V
$\triangle$VthN (0 - 5 v) = _____ V		$\triangle$VthP (0 - 5v) = _____ V
γN (0 - 2 v) = _____		γP (0 - 2v) = _____
γN (0 - 5 v) = _____		γP (0 - 5v) = _____
γN (avg) = _____		γP (avg) = _____

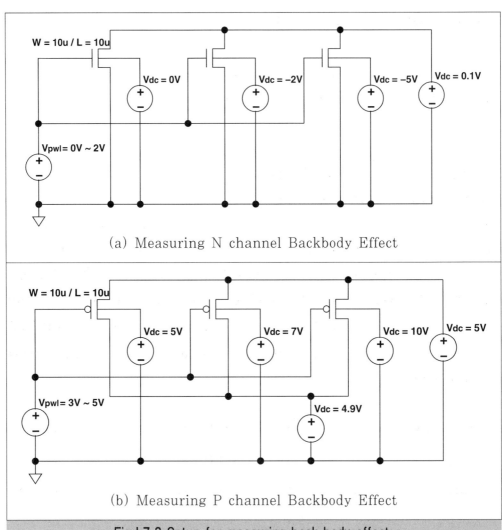

(a) Measuring N channel Backbody Effect

(b) Measuring P channel Backbody Effect

Fig.L7.3 Setup for measuring back body effect.

Step 4 Measuring Channel Length Modulations

λIds (lambda, channel length modulation). Plot the Ids (Y axis) vs. Vds (X axis) of a transistor (W=10 μm, L=10 μm) with the drain connected to the Vds power supply and the gate tied to the Vgs power supply. Tie the body to ground. Let Vds vary from 2 to 4 volts. Set Vgs to a constant of 2.0 volts. The slope of the straight line in saturation will be equal to λIds where Ids is the average value of the current between the Vds=2 and 4 volts.

$$\lambda N \; = \; \rule{3cm}{0.4pt} \qquad\qquad \lambda P \; = \; \rule{3cm}{0.4pt}$$

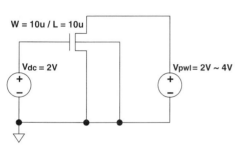

(a) Measuring Channel Length
Modulation of NMOS

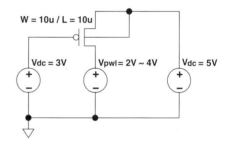

(b) Measuring Channel Length
Modulation of PMOS

Fig.L7.4 Setup for measuring channel length modulations.

Chapter IX. Data Management and CAD Tools

9.1 Directory Structure and File Management

When developing any VLSI designs you are usually dealing with a large number of files of different formats, often spread over many storage devices and being worked on by a number of people. A project can very quickly become a mess. Prior planning and organization is paramount. Almost all of these problems stem from inadequate file management. It is essential that you adopt a system that all team members agree to abide by. What follows are some general conventions and guidelines.

■ Backup Everything ... Often

Backup all your files regularly to a central disk or disks. Make one person only responsible for backing up the team's work and storing it safely. Also, when working on a file, do not continually save over the same file - choose "Save As" and increment a 2-digit number prefixed to the filename. This ensures different versions of the same file are ordered alphabetically in a directory listing That way you'll always have a previous version to go back to if there's a problem, e.g.:

    file_01.prj
    file_02.prj
    file_03.prj ... etc

When the file is finished, remove the suffix e.g.:

    file.prj

■ File Naming Conventions

In addition to the above advice you should get into the habit of naming your files in a way that makes them easy to find, groups similar files together in a directory listing and is compatible with all file systems. These are the golden rules:

- Use meaningful filenames.
- Use all lowercase characters.
- Use underscore _ instead of spaces: Spaces will cause problems on the Internet and other platforms.

■ Logical Directory Structure

Avoid the temptation of either saving everything into one directory or saving files to the directory that the application defaults to. Setup your own directory structure and ensure everything gets saved into the correct folder, e.g.:

```
* project
   - layout
        models
        library
        scripts
        rules
        data
   - schematic
        data
        scripts
   - docs
```

Notice that by using prefixes and suffixes in your filenames, different groups of elements are easy to find as they are ordered alphabetically. This becomes increasingly important as your project grows in size and complexity.

9.2 File Management and Revision Control Systems

■ File Management

Throughout the course of a project, there are teams of people working together and in parallel on many different aspects of the design. Many different kinds of data are created, revised, shared, and deleted very dynamically and quickly. The data can be layout data, but also includes schematics, setup files, documentation, and many other kinds. Database management is a process supported by an infrastructure that fundamentally provides the following features and benefits:

Version control: Each file that is managed should have a version associated with it.

Version history: Histories of all database objects should be tracked.

Data sharing: Data must be shared, and this should be done in a systematic way. Changes to shared cells must not affect work in progress that uses the cells.

Database integrity: Protection against inadvertent deletion or database corruption. Examples of database corruption would be missing cells referenced in a hierarchical design or two cells of the same name in two different places on the computer system.

In a practical sense of designing an IC there are a few basic concepts that make the system work. The function of the database management is to ensure the following:

- Generally, there is a one-to-one correspondence between a circuit and layout design.
- Shared or lower level cells are frozen before being used by other team members.
- Only one person is allowed to change a cell at any given time.
- During the time a cell is being changed, other team members can use an older version.
- New versions of objects are announced and communicated as required.

Proper database management relies on a computer system that recognizes groups of users so that authentication of the person accessing data is possible. The access rights of the data that exists on the system should be specified for three groups of user, depending on the type and application of the data:

Public access: Everyone-necessary for global data such as CAD software.

Group access: Team members-limits and identifies data specific to one project.

Owner access: An individual person who last modified or manipulated the data.

■ Revision Control Systems

A version control system automates the storage, retrieval, logging, identification, and merging of document revisions. Version control is most useful for text that is revised frequently, such as programs, documentation, graphics, papers, and so on. The UNIX operating system provides the following two version control systems with slightly different features [BLN]:

Source Code Control System (SCCS), and

Revision Control System (RCS):

The two tools, RCS and SCCS are probably enough for the designer who is working with relatively simple, single platform projects. Functionally RCS and SCCS are practically equal, with RCS having a bit more features since it continues to be updated. Editing either RCS or SCCS files is a bad idea because mistakes are so easy to make and so fatal to the history of the file.

Using RCS or SCCS lets you keep your source files in a common library and maintain control over them. Both systems provide easy-to-use command-line interfaces. Knowing the basic commands lets you check in the source file to be modified into a version control file that contains all of the revisions of that source file. When you want to check out a version control file for editing, the system retrieves the revision or revisions you specify from the library and creates a working file for you to use.

9.3 Scheduling

Scheduling the layout of a cell, block, or chip is in general a matter of experience. Forecasting a project schedule is a complex task that depends on many factors: tools, flows, hardware, design team experience, training, resources, holidays, sick leave, process changes, etc. In our experience the best way to accelerate any schedule is not faster computers or better software, but increased expertise of the design team [CLN].

First of all, the considerations are below for scheduling the layout of a cell:
- Number of transistors.
- Number of signals.
- Cell type-does it have a template to work from, or is it brand new?
- Special requirements such as minimum size, minimum capacitance, etc.

In all cases of scheduling it is important to think about the speed of an *average* designer and not the best performer, because the schedule has to reflect the reality of a varied design team. Note that the type of cell and the special requirements really affect the relative time it takes to complete the cell.

Secondly, there are different considerations for blocks:
- Number of components-cells, small blocks, random gates.
- Number of busses, signals, and power grid requirements.
- Special requirements-symmetry, crosstalk, minimum RC, timing.
- Size limitation.
- Routing layers available-for example, only three out of five may be a limitation.

Finally, designers should define the factors that affect scheduling for a full chip:

- *Experience level of team*-Does the team have enough experienced people?
- *Change*-Evaluate the risk of certain key parameters changing over the project. For example, pad positions and even design rules are subject to change over the course of a long project.
- *Reuse*-Can we leverage experience and layout designs that were done before?
- *Design complexity*-Number of critical blocks, signals and/ or busses.
- *External factors*-Is the team collocated or is it a joint design project with outsiders?
- *Third-party blocks*-How easy will it be to import a block from an intellectual property (IP) provider?
- *Methodologies*-Are there any new flows and/or tools that have to be introduced?
- *CAD support*-Does the project team get CAD support? What is the priority of the project?
- *Team size*-A large team may not be as productive as a small one because of communication and management overhead.
- *Work day*-Is overtime assumed or planned for? Sick leave, bereavement, vacation time, seasonal restrictions.

9.4 Computer Aided Design (CAD) Tools

VLSI circuits featuring many thousands of transistors on a single chip have become essential building blocks of modern digital electronic systems, ranging from computers to consumer goods. The design of an entire system can be achieved at many different refinement levels from the most detailed layout to the most abstract architectures. Given the complexity that is demanded at all levels, computers are increasingly used to aid this design at each step. Thus, without modern computer-aided design techniques, today's microchip designs would be impossible to create. The design cycle for an IC follows a number of main stages: schematic capture, functional simulation, physical layout, test simulation, and design verification, before the design is released for fabrication. Thus, CAD is used for geometric modeling, analysis, testing, drafting, and documentation. It may one day be possible to automatically design reliable and economical VLSI systems from the algorithm level through the fabrication of a circuit. To realize this potential, advances in CAD tools for VLSI must keep pace with the capabilities of fabrication technology [RUB].

9.4.1   Tools related to Physical Design

Today's CAD methods speed the process of physical design by automatically translating specifications from the chip's behavioral or structural description to its physical layout. The designer uses automatic layout techniques to quickly map the structural representation into a circuit's physical representation. Although these techniques result in less erroneous layouts, the layout itself may be less efficient or creative as one produced by a human designer.

A layout editor is used to draw the graphical shapes that define the mask layout. The editor does not check these shapes, so testing must be done to ensure their correctness. Symbolic layout editors can be used to limit the shapes available to the designer, thus minimizing layout errors, but at a cost trade-off in layout density. On the other hand, in the procedural synthesis method, computer programming techniques such as conditionals, loops, variables, and procedure calls are used to create graphical objects. During the synthesis phase of physical design, tools for automatic placement to position components on a layout surface, and routing to interconnect components with wiring create new or improved layouts from earlier structural representations.

Compactors can also be used to automate a circuit's geometric design by moving its components and wires to optimize space. During the optimization steps, the problems of predicting the interconnect contribution to delay, power, area and noise, and handling the signal integrity became the major bottleneck of the synthesis process. As a result, the physical synthesis approaches have to be reexamined and new solutions need to be found. A large number of CAD specialists are necessary to develop these new solutions and tools for physical design automation. There are general aspects of layout CAD tools such as physical synthesis (layout synthesis, partitioning, floorplanning, placement, and routing), verification, and design management.

MyChip Station (MyCAD), Virtuoso (Cadence), Apollo (Avant!)

■ Create Custom Layouts

A layout is basically a drawing of the masks from which a design will be fabricated. Therefore, layout is just as critical as specifying the parameters of a device because it determines whether the device is a working design or not. There are two ways to doing a layout: manual (Layout editor) and automated (Auto-Router). Manual layout usually enables the designer to pack his devices in a smaller area compared to the automated process but it is more tedious. The automated process, on the other hand, is done using standard cells and usually takes more real estate space but it is much faster.

▣ Floorplanners

A floorplanner is used to coordinate placement and routing engines to create a layout floorplan. Floorplanners are discussed extensively because they pose new concepts and challenges for layout design. When used properly, floorplanners can reduce time to market by providing a methodology for top-down design and layout that is correct by construction.

▣ Placers

A placer optimizes the placement of cells or devices using physical and logical constraints. Placers are generally designed to work with specific routers; therefore, it is very important to use a placer and router from the same vendor. This is because the two tools work together to meet the constraints and take advantage of features and information that are known to both tools.

▣ Compactors

A compactor automatically optimizes existing layout and is generally used as an enhancement to an advanced layout editor or symbolic layout tool. The compactor shrinks or enlarges the width and space between polygons with a goal of minimizing the layout to the limits of the process design rules.

▣ Device generators

Device generators are used to generate layout devices such as transistors, via arrays, or logic gates. They typically have an extensive graphical user interface and a highly developed macro language. In some cases the device generator is an enhancement to a layout editor or an independent tool. Without a placer or a router, device generators have very limited value for enhancing productivity.

▣ Silicon compilers

A silicon compiler builds a physical description or layout of a chip from its behavioral description. The designer specifies a design structure, then the circuit's parameters such as functional, electrical, and geometrical parameters are processed by corresponding module compilers. All relevant design rules are stored in a technology file to check the circuit. Timing and logic models are also generated for each component in the circuit. The system then uses placement and routing to form a chip composite. In general, silicon compilers do not have a graphical user interface, as they are used to process a large number of structures.

▣ Design Rule Check (DRC)

The next step in the Design Process is to perform a Design Rule Check, more commonly known as DRC, on the layout. Although designers might be conscious of the design rules when performing the layout, there is a possibility of overlooking and thus violating the design rules. So, the DRC is a step taken to prompt us of any violations. This step is important because the violation of any design rule would result in a higher probability and in some cases an absolute certainty that the fabricated chip does not work as desired.

■ Layout Versus Schematic (LVS) Verification

A successful DRC ensures that the layout passes through the rules designed for faultless fabrication. However, it does not guarantee that it really represents the circuit you desire to fabricate. Therefore, we really need a tool which can compare our layout with the schematic and ensure that it is really a layout for an inverter. One way is to generate a spice netlist from the layout and compae it with the spice netlist for the schematic. This is the essence of the LVS tool.

■ Post Layout Simulation (→ Parameter Extractor)

The parasitic capacitances created according to how your layout is done at times might be critical in affecting the actual performance of your design. In order to get an idea of how the design would work from your layout, you should perform a post-layout simulation from the extracted view. The procedure is identical to that for simulating from the pre-layout simulation.

9.4.2 *Other Tools*

■ Schematic Capture

Whereas hardware-description languages achieve the same result textually, schematic capture tools are used to sketch the circuits on a display screen. Schematic capture tools should have the following features:

ⓐ High integration with the other design tools, so that they all use a common design database and run on the same platform.
ⓑ Multiple modes of design entry.
ⓒ Support of top down and general hierarchical design approaches.

ⓓ Support of industry standard HDLs such as VHDL or Verilog HDL.

ⓔ Netlist capability in a standard format such as Electronic Design Interchange Format (EDIF) for design portability.

Some examples of schematic capture tools include:

MyAnalog Station (MyCAD), Composer (Cadence), Design Architect (Mentor)

▣ Logic & Circuit Simulation Tools

Logic simulation verifies the correct logical operation of a design. The design primitive used at this level must be well characterized. The logic simulation tools should be able to provide mixed-mode simulation such as a combination of behavioral and structural level circuit representations. Mixed mode simulations prove very useful for large designs, where a behavioral model represents one or more big blocks and a block receiving detailed analysis is at gate level representation.

MyLogic Station (MyCAD), Verilog-XL (Cadence), VCS (Synopsys), Vcom,Vsim (Mentor/Model Technology), Quicksim (Mentor)

Circuit simulation simulates at the transistor level. In contrast to switch level simulation, which uses logical models of transistors, circuit simulation uses parametric transistor models for simulation. Lengths and widths of transistor are fed into a polynomial model and used to calculate the behavior of a circuit.

MyAnalog Station (MyCAD), Accusim (Mentor), Hspice (Avanti), Septre (Cadence)

▣ Logic Synthesis

Synthesis programs convert among the different refinement levels of a design. Synthesis tools should have the following features:

ⓐ Two levels of optimization-architectural and gate levels

ⓑ Use of a technology file that uses vendor or user supplied design rules along with a cell library to synthesize and optimize a cell/gate level design

ⓒ Ability to map a design into other vendor design libraries

ⓓ Capability to map into macro cells of the design library

ⓔ Options to optimize for speed, area, power or some combination of the three

Design Compiler (Synopsys), Leonardo Spectrum (Mentor/Exemplar), Autologic (Mentor)

▣ Tools related to Test

CAD tests a circuit design by simulating it, rather than constructing expensive hardware. Testing simulates operating conditions and detects faults at the circuit level which may affect performance. A set of test vectors is developed in a test language to detect a circuit's input and output behavior. Automatic test pattern generators (ATPG) can automatically develop a set of tests for a particular circuit, although they require some restrictions on the design. Fault simulators grade tests by simulating a circuit, assuming a fault, and verifying that the test vectors propagate the differences as a result of that fault as seen in the outputs. The percentage of faults detected indicates the quality of the test. Testing indicates the yield, or number of functioning chips [WAE].

Test Compiler (Synopsys), TetraMAX (Synopsys)

▣ Integrated Environment Tools

A modern CAD system provides an integrated suite of facilities to support all design stages (Schematic Capture, Layout Editor, DRC Checker and other design tools), with an appropriate mixture of automatic and user-controlled processing at each.

IC Station (Mentor), Opus (Cadence)

References

[RUB] Steven M. Rubin, *Computer Aids for VLSI Design*, Second Edition, Addison-Wesley Publishing Company, 1994.

[CLN] Dan Clein, *CMOS IC LAYOUT: Concepts, Methodologies, and Tools*, Newnes, 1999.

[BLN] Don Bolinger, Mike Loukides, and Tan Bronson, *Applying RCS and SCCS: From Source Control to Project Control*, Thomson Learning, 1994.

LAB8. Analog Circuit Design

Linear integrated circuits are widely used, and mixed-mode systems containing both linear and logic circuits are increasingly the trend with applications in consumer products, communications, smart power and many other areas. One of the important circuit blocks in an operational amplifier (OP Amp) is the linear bias circuitry. Depending on the design of the OP Amp, bias currents may be required. In this lab, you will construct a circuit that generates bias currents so that you can learn how to design these circuits, learn how they work, and be able to design the required bias circuitry.

Pre-Lab: CMOS Linear Circuits

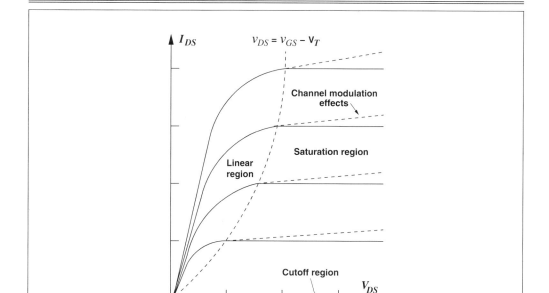

Fig.L8.1 VI characteristic of NMOS.

This pre-lab describes a number of circuit techniques based on CMOS for implementing typical linear circuits. In linear circuits, MOSFETS are usually biased into the saturation region (Fig.L8.1) in which $I_d = 0.5 \ \beta(V_{gs} - V_t)^2 \ (1 + \lambda \ V_{ds})$, where $\beta = . \mu\varepsilon/T_{ox} \ (W/L)$, and λ = channel length modulation factor.

We are now interested in small signal models at a suitable quiescent point.

Mutual conductance: $g_m = \partial i_d / \partial V_{gs} = \text{sqrt}(2\beta I_d)(1 + \lambda \ V_{ds}) \approx \text{sqrt}(2\beta I_d)$.

Channel conductance: $g_d = \partial i_d / \partial V_{ds} = \lambda I_d/(1 +. \lambda I_d) \approx \lambda I_d$

ⓐ MOSFET as a resistor

Resistors implemented in polysilicon or diffusion occupy in large areas. In the case where conserving area is more important than linearity, active resistors that need small area are preferred:

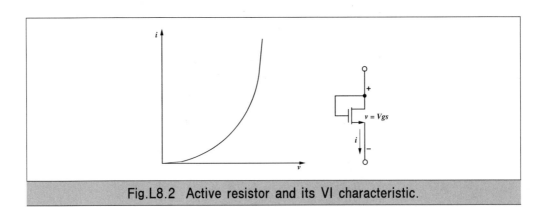

Fig.L8.2 Active resistor and its VI characteristic.

Couple G to D. Hence $V_{ds} = V_{gs}$.

Thus, $V_{ds} > V_{gs} - V_t$, i.e. device is in saturation, and if channel length modulation factor is negligible,

$$I_d = 0.5 \ \beta(V_{gs} - V_t)^2 \quad (Eq.8.1).$$

Thus, small signal resistance $\partial V_{gs} / \partial i_d = 1/g_m = 1/\sqrt{2\beta I_d}$

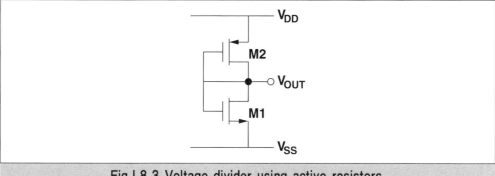

Fig.L8.3 Voltage divider using active resistors.

In Fig.L8.3, both devices of the voltage divider are in the saturation region and drain currents are identical. Thus, W/L ratios for each device are solved using equation (Eq.8.1).

❶ Current sources and sinks

A current source/sink is a 2-terminal device. An ideal source/sink has infinite output resistance.

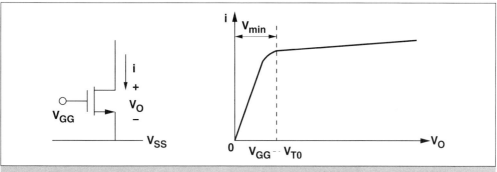

Fig.L8.4 A basic setup of a current source and its VI characteristic.

V_{GG} is held fixed by the potential divider (Fig.L8.3). The current substantially is independent of V_O.

Assume:

Vo 〉 V_{min} = V_{GG} - V_t - V_{SS}.

Current i = 0.5 $\beta(V_{GG} - V_t)2$ (say, 100 μ A)

The resistance at output: $r = 1/g_d = (1+\lambda V_{ds})/ \lambda I_d = 1/\lambda I_d$ (typ. 1MΩ at 100μ A)

In practical circuits, it may be necessary to increase the output resistance r. One solution in Fig.L8.5(a) is to insert additional resistance R into the source, using a passive device. This enhances the effective output resistance of the current source. Note the new output resistance: $r' = (1 + g_mR) / g_d$.

Fig.L8.5(b) shows a current sink using an active voltage divider to set the bias. Now the new output resistance is about $g_{m2} / (g_{d1}{}^*g_{d2})$.

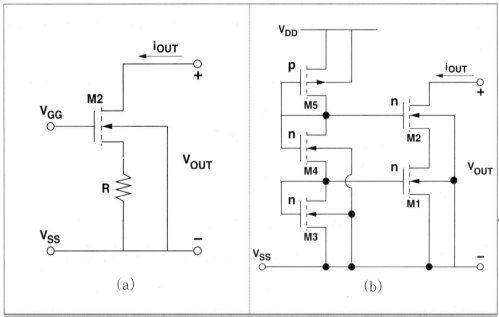

Fig.L8.5 Alternatives: (a) Source degenerated current source and (b) Cascode current source

ⓒ Current mirror source

Fig.L8.6 shows a basic current mirror where the current (I_R) is mirrored to the other branch (I_1). In this lab, you must use only CMOS transistors and a power supply to generate this reference current.

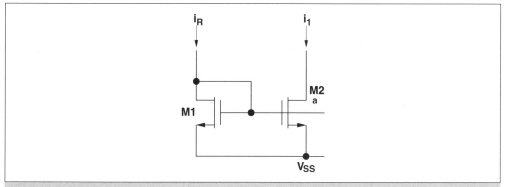

Fig.L8.6 A basic current mirror.

M_1 is in saturation since $V_{ds1} = V_{gs1}$

Assume M_2 saturated: i.e. $V_{ds2} = V_{ds1}$

Determine the ratio i_1/i_R =

$$\frac{(L_1\,W_2 \times \mu_2 \varepsilon t_{ox1})(V_{gs} - V_t)(1+\lambda V_{ds2})}{(L_2\,W_1 \times \mu_1 \varepsilon t_{ox2})(V_{gs} - V_t)(1+\lambda V_{ds1})} = \frac{(L_1\,W_2)(1+\lambda V_{ds2})}{(L_2\,W_1)(1+\lambda V_{ds1})} \quad (Eq.8.2)$$

Using the assumption that $V_{ds2}=V_{ds1}$ (not always justified in practice): $i_1/i_R = L_1W_2/W_1L_2$ i.e. geometry alone determines the ratio: i_1/i_R

To adjust the reference current (I_R) in the circuit of Fig.L8.6, we will use voltage divider using active resistors in Fig.L8.3. Since these transistors in the voltage divider act like diodes, the larger W/L is, the larger I_R is. If M_2 has a W/L ratio that is 10 times W/L of M_1, then I_1 will be 10 times I_R as shown in Eq.8.2 since M_2 and M_1 have the same $|V_{GS}|$. Note that for the given specifications in the following procedure, hand calculations of transistor sizes should be preformed as a first step to this design.

Procedure: Current Mirror Design

Step 1 **Current Mirror Current Source**

Design a simple current source for $15\mu A$ of current as shown in Fig.L8.7. We shall assume the following values:

$V_{DD}=5V$; $V_{tn}=+0.7V$; $\mu_n/t_{ox}=\_\_ A/V^2$ (Lab.7); $_n=\_\_V^{-1}$(Lab.7).
$V_{SS}=0V$; $V_{tp}=-0.7V$; $\mu_p/t_{ox}=\_\_ A/V^2$ (Lab.7); $_p=\_\_V^{-1}$(Lab.7).

Set V1 = 1 volt and size all of the transistors. The minimum values of transistor size $W=3\mu$, $L=3\mu$ and the resolution   is 1μ .These restrictions on the size of W and L apply to all steps in this lab. Always try to use the minimum size and adjust upward to minimize the overall size of your circuit. Although it is always possible to make transistors meet the W/L ratio determined by hand calculations, you will have to analyze the tradeoff between size and accuracy. For example, if you calculate a W/L ratio of 10.13, you could make this transistor by setting $W=1013\mu$ and $L=100\mu$, but that is a huge transistor. You would probably be better off using $W=30\mu$ and $L=3\mu$. You can assume that there is no back body effect. Use AD = AS = 3 * W, PD = PS = W + 6μ .

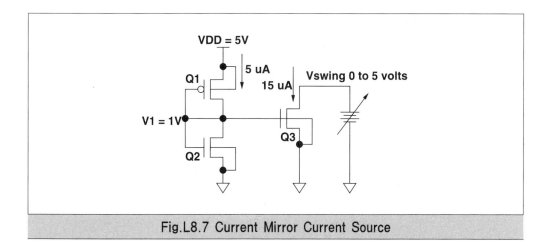

Fig.L8.7 Current Mirror Current Source

You are to first do a manual calculation for each transistor. Mark these values on the schematic. Then calculate the effective output resistance. Input this circuit in LayEd of MyChip. Note that you must use 4-terminal devices with proper bulk connections for any transistor and its source terminal is connected to the power supply rail (ground/nMOS or VDD/pMOS). Run a simulation by sweeping the output voltage from 0 to 5 volts. Measure the slope of the line. Turn in your schematic and plot of the sweep. These results should be described in your report along with the relevant equations used for hand calculations.

Rout (calculated) _____

Rout (Simulated) _____

Minimum usable voltage for current source (knee of curve)_____

Step 2 Source Degenerated Current Source

Same as Step 1, except that you must use Fig.L8.8 with resistor R1 to give source degeneration. Set the value of R1 such that the output resistance is double the resistance that you found in Step 1.

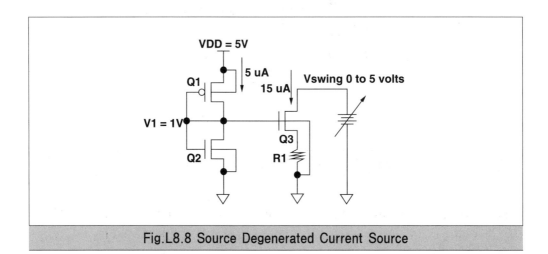

Fig.L8.8 Source Degenerated Current Source

Assume that Q3 is the same size as Q3 in Step 1. You must recalculate the size of Q1 and Q2 to account for the voltage on R1. The same restrictions on the minimum size of W and L apply here. Turn in your schematic and plot of the sweep. These results should be described in your report along with the relevant equations used for hand calculations.

Rout (Step 1: calculated) _____

Rout (Step 2: calculated) _____

Rout (Step 3: simulated) _____

Minimum usable voltage for current source (knee of curve)_____

Step 3 | **Cascode Current Source**

Similar to Step 2, except that you must use Fig.L8.9. Size each transistor and mark the size on the schematic. Do an MySPICE simulation. Turn in your schematic and plot of the sweep. These results should be described in your report along with the relevant equations used for hand calculations.

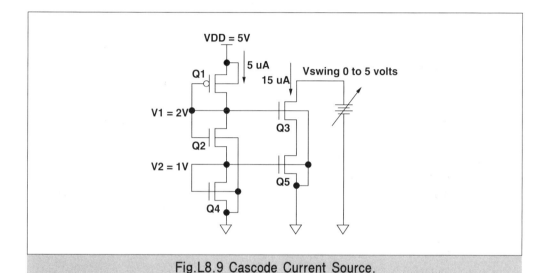

Fig.L8.9 Cascode Current Source.

*I*NDEX

MyCAD, Inc.

528 E Weddell Drive, Suite 3
Sunnyvale, CA 94089, USA
Tel : (408) 745-6785
Fax : (408) 745-6783
E-mail : sales@mycad.com
support@mycad.com
http://www.mycad.com